# Level 1

# ¡Avancemos!

## Unit 1 Resource Book

**HOLT McDOUGAL**
a division of Houghton Mifflin Harcourt

Fine Art Acknowledgments

Page 117 *Music* (2005), Xavier Cortada. Acrylic on canvas, 60″ x 96″. Courtesy of the artist.

Page 118 *Las hermanas Woloff* (1996), Marta Sánchez. Courtesy of the artist.

Page 119 *Mis hermanos* (1976), Jesse Trevino. Acrylic on canvas, 48″ x 70″. Smithsonian American Art Museum, Washington, DC/Art Resource, NY.

Page 120 *Flower Sellers*, Alfredo Ramos Martínez. Oil on canvas. Image courtesy of Louis Stern Fine Arts, West Hollywood, CA. Christie's Images/SuperStock.

ISBN-13: 978-0-618-76609-3
ISBN-10: 0-618-76609-X      13 14 15 16 17 1689 19 18 17 16 15
4500531933
Internet: www.holtmcdougal.com

HOLT McDOUGAL

# ¡Avancemos!

# Table of Contents

# To the Teacher

Welcome to *¡Avancemos!* This exciting new Spanish program from McDougal Littell has been designed to provide you—the teacher of today's foreign language classroom—with comprehensive pedagogical support.

## PRACTICE WITH A PURPOSE

Activities throughout the program begin by establishing clear goals. Look for the **¡Avanza!** arrow that uses student-friendly language to lead the way towards achievable goals. Built-in self-checks in the student text (**Para y piensa:** Did you get it?) offer the chance to assess student progress throughout the lesson. Both the student text and the workbooks offer abundant leveled practice to match varied student needs.

## CULTURE AS A CORNERSTONE

*¡Avancemos!* celebrates the cultural diversity of the Spanish-speaking world by motivating students to think about similarities and contrasts among different Spanish-speaking cultures. Essential questions encourage thoughtful discussion and comparison between different cultures.

## LANGUAGE LEARNING THAT LASTS

The program presents topics in manageable chunks that students will be able to retain and recall. "Recycle" topics are presented frequently so students don't forget material from previous lessons. Previously learned content is built upon and reinforced across the different levels of the program.

## TIME-SAVING TEACHER TOOLS

Simplify your planning with McDougal Littell's exclusive teacher resources: the all-inclusive EasyPlanner DVD-ROM, ready-made Power Presentations, and the McDougal Littell Assessment System.

# Unit Resource Book

Each Unit Resource Book supports a unit of *¡Avancemos!* The Unit Resource Books provide a wide variety of materials to support, practice, and expand on the material in the *¡Avancemos!* student text.

*Components* **Following is a list of components included in each Unit Resource Book:**

## BACK TO SCHOOL RESOURCES (UNIT 1 ONLY)

Review and start-up activities to support the **Lección preliminar** of the textbook.

## DID YOU GET IT? RETEACHING & PRACTICE COPYMASTERS

 If students' performance on the **Para y piensa** self-check for a section does not meet your expectations, consider assigning the corresponding Did You Get It? Reteaching and Practice Copymasters. These copymasters provide extensive reteaching and additional practice for every vocabulary and grammar presentation section in *¡Avancemos!* Each vocabulary and grammar section has a corresponding three-page copymaster. The first page of the copymaster reteaches the subject material in a fresh manner. Immediately following this presentation page are two pages of practice exercises that help the student master the topic. The practice pages have engaging contexts and structures to retain students' attention.

## PRACTICE GAMES

These games provide fun practice of the vocabulary and grammar just taught. They are targeted in scope so that each game practices a specific area of the **lesson**: *Práctica de vocabulario, Vocabulario en contexto, Práctica de gramática, Gramática en contexto, Todo junto, Repaso de la lección*, and the lesson's cultural information.

### Video and audio resources

## VIDEO ACTIVITIES

These two-page copymasters accompany the Vocabulary Video and each scene of the **Telehistoria** in Levels 1 and 2 and the **Gran desafío** in Level 3. The pre-viewing activity asks students to activate prior knowledge about a theme or subject related to the scene they will watch. The viewing activity is a simple activity for students to complete as they watch the video. The post-viewing activity gives students the opportunity to demonstrate comprehension of the video episode.

## VIDEO SCRIPTS

This section provides the scripts of each video feature in the unit.

## AUDIO SCRIPTS

This section contains scripts for all presentations and activities that have accompanying audio in the student text as well as in the two workbooks (*Cuaderno: práctica por niveles* and *Cuaderno para hispanohablantes*) and the assessment program.

### Culture resources

## MAP/CULTURE ACTIVITIES

This section contains a copymaster with geography and culture activities based on the Unit Opener in the textbook.

## FINE ART ACTIVITIES

The fine art activities in every lesson ask students to analyze pieces of art that have been selected as representative of the unit location country. These copymasters can be used in conjunction with the full-color fine art transparencies in the Unit Transparency Book.

### Home-school connection

## FAMILY LETTERS & FAMILY INVOLVEMENT ACTIVITIES

This section is designed to help increase family support of the students' study of Spanish. The family letter keeps families abreast of the class's progress, while the family involvement activities let students share their Spanish language skills with their families in the context of a game or fun activity.

## ABSENT STUDENT COPYMASTERS

The Absent Student Copymasters enable students who miss part of a **lesson** to go over the material on their own. The checkbox format allows teachers to choose and indicate exactly what material the student should complete. The Absent Student Copymasters also offer strategies and techniques to help students understand new or challenging information.

# Core Ancillaries in the ¡Avancemos! Program

**Leveled workbooks**

## CUADERNO: PRÁCTICA POR NIVELES

This core ancillary is a leveled practice workbook to supplement the student text. It is designed for use in the classroom or as homework. Students who can complete the activities correctly should be able to pass the quizzes and tests. Practice is organized into three levels of difficulty, labeled A, B, and C. Level B activities are designed to practice vocabulary, grammar, and other core concepts at a level appropriate to most of your students. Students who require more structure can complete Level A activities, while students needing more of a challenge should be encouraged to complete the activities in Level C. Each level provides a different degree of linguistic support, yet requires students to know and handle the same vocabulary and grammar content.

The following sections are included in *Cuaderno: práctica por niveles* for each **lesson**:

| | |
|---|---|
| Vocabulario A, B, C | Escuchar A, B, C |
| Gramática 1 A, B, C | Leer A, B, C |
| Gramática 2 A, B, C | Escribir A, B, C |
| Integración: Hablar | Cultura A, B, C |
| Integración: Escribir | |

## CUADERNO PARA HISPANOHABLANTES

This core ancillary provides leveled practice for heritage learners of Spanish. Level A is for heritage learners who hear Spanish at home but who may speak little Spanish themselves. Level B is for those who speak some Spanish but don't read or write it yet and who may lack formal education in Spanish. Level C is for heritage learners who have had some formal schooling in Spanish. These learners can read and speak Spanish, but may need further development of their writing skills. The *Cuaderno para hispanohablantes* will ensure that heritage learners practice the same basic grammar, reading, and writing skills taught in the student text. At the same time, it offers additional instruction and challenging practice designed specifically for students with prior knowledge of Spanish.

The following sections are included in *Cuaderno para hispanohablantes* for each **lesson**:

| | |
|---|---|
| Vocabulario A, B, C | Integración: Hablar |
| Vocabulario adicional | Integración: Escribir |
| Gramática 1 A, B, C | Lectura A, B, C |
| Gramática 2 A, B, C | Escritura A, B, C |
| Gramática adicional | Cultura A, B, C |

# Other Ancillaries

## ASSESSMENT PROGRAM

For each level of *¡Avancemos!*, there are four complete assessment options. Every option assesses students' ability to use the lesson and unit vocabulary and grammar, as well as assessing reading, writing, listening, speaking, and cultural knowledge. The on-level tests are designed to assess the language skills of most of your students. Modified tests provide more support, explanation and scaffolding to enable students with learning difficulties to produce language at the same level as their peers. Pre-AP* tests build the test-taking skills essential to success on Advanced Placement tests. The assessments for heritage learners are all in Spanish, and take into account the strengths that native speakers bring to language learning.

In addition to leveled lesson and unit tests, there is a complete array of vocabulary, culture, and grammar quizzes. All tests include scoring rubrics and point teachers to specific resources for remediation.

## UNIT TRANSPARENCY BOOKS—1 PER UNIT

Each transparency book includes:

- Map Atlas Transparencies (Unit 1 only)
- Unit Opener Map Transparencies
- Fine Art Transparencies
- Vocabulary Transparencies
- Grammar Presentation Transparencies
- Situational Transparencies with Label Overlay (plus student copymasters)
- Warm Up Transparencies
- Student Book and Workbook Answer Transparencies

## LECTURAS PARA TODOS

A workbook-style reader, *Lecturas para todos*, offers all the readings from the student text as well as additional literary readings in an interactive format. In addition to the readings, they contain reading strategies, comprehension questions, and tools for developing vocabulary.

There are four sections in each *Lecturas para todos*:

- *¡Avancemos!* readings with annotated skill-building support
- *Literatura adicional*—additional literary readings
- Academic and Informational Reading Development
- Test Preparation Strategies

* AP and the Advanced Placement Program are registered trademarks of the College Entrance Examination Board, which was not involved in the production of and does not endorse this product.

## LECTURAS PARA HISPANOHABLANTES

*Lecturas para hispanohablantes* offers additional cultural readings for heritage learners and a rich selection of literary readings. All readings are supported by reading strategies, comprehension questions, tools for developing vocabulary, plus tools for literary analysis.

There are four sections in each *Lecturas para hispanohablantes*:

- *En voces* cultural readings with annotated skill-building support

- *Literatura adicional*—high-interest readings by prominent authors from around the Spanish-speaking world. Selections were chosen carefully to reflect the diversity of experiences Spanish-speakers bring to the classroom.

- Bilingual Academic and Informational Reading Development

- Bilingual Test Preparation Strategies, for success on standardized tests in English

## COMIC BOOKS

These fun, motivating comic books are written in a contemporary, youthful style with full-color illustrations. Each comic uses the target language students are learning. There is one 32-page comic book for each level of the program.

## TPRS: TEACHING PROFICIENCY THROUGH READING AND STORYTELLING

This book includes an up-to-date guide to TPRS and TPRS stories written by Piedad Gutiérrez that use *¡Avancemos!* lesson-specific vocabulary.

## MIDDLE SCHOOL RESOURCE BOOK

- Practice activities to support the 1b Bridge lesson
- Diagnostic and Bridge Unit Tests
- Transparencies
  - Vocabulary Transparencies
  - Grammar Transparencies
  - Answer Transparencies for the Student Text
  - Bridge Warm Up Transparencies
- Audio CDs

## LESSON PLANS

- Lesson Plans with suggestions for modifying instruction
- Core and Expansion options clearly noted
- IEP suggested modifications
- Substitute teacher lesson plans

## BEST PRACTICES TOOLKIT

### Strategies for Effective Teaching

- Research-based Learning Strategies
- Language Learning that Lasts: Teaching for Long-term Retention
- Culture as a Cornerstone/Cultural Comparisons
- English Grammar Connection
- Building Vocabulary
- Developing Reading Skills
- Differentiation
- Best Practices in Teaching Heritage Learners
- Assessment (including Portfolio Assessment, Reteaching and Remediation)
- Best Practices Swap Shop: Favorite Activities for Teaching Reading, Writing, Listening, Speaking
- Reading, Writing, Listening, and Speaking Strategies in the World Languages classroom
- ACTFL Professional Development Articles
- Thematic Teaching
- Best Practices in Middle School

### Using Technology in the World Languages Classroom

### Tools for Motivation

- Games in the World Languages Classroom
- Teaching Proficiency through Reading and Storytelling
- Using Comic Books for Motivation

### Pre-AP and International Baccalaureate

- International Baccalaureate
- Pre-AP

### Graphic Organizer Transparencies

- Teaching for Long-term Retention
- Teaching Culture
- Building Vocabulary
- Developing Reading Skills

# Absent Student Copymasters—Tips for Students

## LISTENING TO CDS AT HOME

- Open your text, workbook, or class notes to the corresponding pages that relate to the audio you will listen to. Read the assignment directions if there are any. Do these steps before listening to the audio selections.

- Listen to the CD in a quiet place. Play the CD loudly enough so that you can hear everything clearly. Keep focused. Play a section several times until you understand it. Listen carefully. Repeat aloud with the CD. Try to sound like the people on the CD. Stop the CD when you need to do so.

- If you are lost, stop the CD. Replay it and look at your notes. Take a break if you are not focusing. Return and continue after a break. Work in short periods of time: 5 or 10 minutes at a time so that you remain focused and energized.

## QUESTION/ANSWER SELECTIONS

- If there is a question/answer selection, read the question aloud several times. Write down the question. Highlight the key words, verb endings, and any new words. Look up new words and write their meaning. Then say everything aloud.

- One useful strategy for figuring out questions is to put parentheses around groups of words that go together. For example: **(¿Cuántos niños)(van)(al estadio)(a las tres?)** Read each group of words one at a time. Check for meaning. Write out answers. Highlight key words and verb endings. Say the question aloud. Read the answer aloud. Ask yourself if you wrote what you meant.

- Be sure to say everything aloud several times before moving on to the next question. Check for spelling, verb endings, and accent marks.

## FLASHCARDS FOR VOCABULARY

- If you have Internet access, go to ClassZone at classzone.com. All the vocabulary taught in *¡Avancemos!* is available on electronic flashcards. Look for the flashcards in the *¡Avancemos!* section of ClassZone.

- If you don't have Internet access, write the Spanish word or phrase on one side of a 3″ × 5″ card, and the English translation on the other side. Illustrate your flashcards when possible. Be sure to highlight any verb endings, accent marks, or other special spellings that will need a bit of extra attention.

## GRAMMAR ACTIVITIES

- Underline or highlight all verb endings and adjective agreements. For example: **Nosotros comemos pollo rico.**

- Underline or highlight infinitive endings: **trabajar**.

- Underline or highlight accented letters. Say aloud and be louder on the accented letters. Listen carefully for the loudness. This will remind you where to write your accent mark. For example: **lápiz, lápices, árbol, árboles**

- When writing a sentence, be sure to ask yourself, "What do I mean? What am I trying to say?" Then check your sentence to be sure that you wrote what you wanted to say.

- Mark patterns with a highlighter. For example, for stem-changing verbs, you can draw a "boot" around the letters that change:

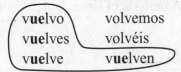

| | |
|---|---|
| vuelvo | volvemos |
| vuelves | volvéis |
| vuelve | vuelven |

## READING AND CULTURE SECTIONS

- Read the strategy box. Copy the graphic organizer so you can fill it out as you read.

- Look at the title and subtitles before you begin to read. Then look at and study any photos and read the captions. Translate the captions only if you can't understand them at all. Before you begin to read, guess what the selection will be about. What do you think that you will learn? What do you already know about this topic?

- Read any comprehension questions before beginning to read the paragraphs. This will help you focus on the upcoming reading selection. Copy the questions and highlight key words.

- Reread one or two of the questions and then go to the text. Begin to read the selection carefully. Read it again. On a sticky note, write down the appropriate question number next to where the answer lies in the text. This will help you keep track of what the questions have asked you and will help you focus when you go back to reread it later, perhaps in preparation for a quiz or test.

- Highlight any new words. Make a list or flashcards of new words. Look up their meanings. Study them. Quiz yourself or have a partner quiz you. Then go back to the comprehension questions and check your answers from memory. Look back at the text if you need to verify your answers.

## PAIRED PRACTICE EXERCISES

- If there is an exercise for partners, practice both parts at home.

- If no partner is available, write out both scripts and practice both roles aloud. Highlight and underline key words, verb endings, and accent marks.

## WRITING PROJECTS

- Brainstorm ideas before writing.

- Make lists of your ideas.

- Put numbers next to the ideas to determine the order in which you want to write about them.

- Group your ideas into paragraphs.

- Skip lines in your rough draft.

- Have a partner read your work and give you feedback on the meaning and language structure.

- Set it aside and reread it at least once before doing a final draft. Double-check verb endings, adjective agreements, and accents.

- Read it once again to check that you said what you meant to say.

- Be sure to have a title and any necessary illustrations or bibliography.

# Hola, ¿qué tal? *Práctica A*

| ¡AVANZA! | **Goal:** Practice expressions of greeting and farewell. |

**1** Circle the correct word to complete the following expressions.

1. Hola, ¿qué _____ ?
   a. estás
   b. tú
   c. tal
   d. cómo

2. _____ mañana, Esteban.
   a. Luego
   b. Hasta
   c. Buenas
   d. Gracias

3. Buenos días, Ana. ¿ _____ estás?
   a. Cómo
   b. Qué
   c. Más
   d. Tú

4. Más o _____ . ¿Y tú?
   a. más
   b. menos
   c. mal
   d. tardes

**2** Fill in the blanks with the word that best completes the expression.

1. ¡Hola! ¿ _____ tal?

2. _____ días, señor García.

3. Buenas tardes, señora Ramos. ¿Cómo _____ usted?

4. _____ noches, Diana. ¿Cómo estás _____ ?

5. Muy _____ , gracias.

**3** Practice the following dialogues with a partner.

**Dialogue 1: between friends**

—Buenos días, _____ .

—¡Hola! Buenos días.

—¿Qué tal?

—Bien. ¿Cómo estás hoy?

—Más o menos. ¿Y tú?

—Regular. Hasta luego, _____ .

—¡Adiós!

**Dialogue 2: between professionals**

—Buenas tardes, Sr/a. _____ .

—Buenas tardes. ¿Cómo está usted?

—Muy bien, gracias. ¿Y usted?

—Muy bien.

—Hasta mañana, Sr/a _____ .

—Adiós, Sr/a ___ . Hasta mañana.

—Adiós.

# Hola, ¿qué tal? *Práctica B*

> **¡AVANZA!** **Goal:** Practice expressions of greeting and farewell.

**❶** Underline the most logical answer to complete the dialogue.

1. **Juan:** Hola, ¿qué tal?
   **Miguel:** (Adiós, señorita. / Muy bien, ¿y tú?)

2. **Esteban:** Buenas noches, Sr. García.
   **Sr. García:** (Hasta mañana, Esteban. / Regular. ¿Y tú?)

3. **Diana:** Buenas tardes. ¿Cómo está usted?
   **Sra. Ramos:** (Muy bien, gracias. / Hasta luego, Diana.)

4. **Sra. Acevedo:** Buenos días, Ana. (¿Cómo estás? / Hasta luego.)
   **Ana:** Muy bien. ¿Y usted?

**❷** Complete the dialogue with a logical expression.

1. **Miguel:** ¡Hola, Juan! ¿Cómo estás?

   **Juan:** _____

2. **Sra. Ramos:** Buenas noches, Sr. Ortega.

   **Sr. Ortega:** _____

3. **Ana:** Adiós, Diana.

   **Diana:** _____

4. **Esteban:** _____
   **Ana:** Más o menos. ¿Y tú?

**❸** Practice informal expressions with a partner. Be sure to include a greeting, inquire about how the other person is doing, and say goodbye in your dialogue.

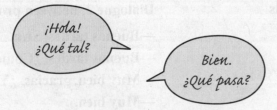

¡Hola! ¿Qué tal?

Bien. ¿Qué pasa?

# Hola, ¿qué tal? *Práctica C*

> **¡AVANZA!**    **Goal:**    Practice expressions of greeting and farewell.

**1** Circle the correct answer to complete the expression.

   **1.** (Hasta / Buenos) días, señora Acevedo. ¿Cómo (está / estás) usted?

   **2.** Buenos (días / tardes), Ramón. ¿Qué (tal / luego)?

   **3.** Hasta (luego / adiós), señor Ortega.

   **4.** ¡Hola, David! ¿(Qué / Cómo) estás (tú / usted)?

   **5.** **Tomás:** ¿Cómo estás?
       **Sofía:** Más o (regular / menos). ¿Y (usted / tú)?

   **6.** Hola, señor Ortega. ¿(Hasta / Cómo) está (usted / tú)?

**2** Diana runs into her teacher, Sra. Acevedo, on her way to the store. Write a brief dialogue between the two on the lines below.

**Sra. Acevedo:** _____

**Diana:** _____

**Sra. Acevedo:** _____

**Diana:** _____

**Sra. Acevedo:** _____

**Diana:** _____

**Sra. Acevedo:** _____

**3** Practice informal expressions with a partner. Be sure to include an informal greeting, inquire about how the other person is doing, and say goodbye in your dialogue. Then find a different partner to practice formal expressions. Be sure to include a formal greeting, inquire about how the other person is doing, and say goodbye in your dialogue.

Hola, Sr/a. ¿Cómo está usted?

Muy bien, ¿y usted?

## ¡Mucho gusto! *Práctica A*

> ¡AVANZA!   **Goal:**  Practice making introductions.

**1** Draw lines to connect the expressions with their correct responses.

    **1.** ¿Cómo te llamas?       **a.** Igualmente.

    **2.** ¿Cómo se llama?        **b.** Se llama Esteban.

    **3.** Le presento a Ana Vega.   **c.** Es Diana.

    **4.** Encantado.            **d.** Me llamo Miguel Luque.

    **5.** ¿Quién es?           **e.** Mucho gusto.

**2** Complete the dialogue with the correct expressions.

**Rosa:** Hola. Me llamo Rosa, ¿y tú?

**Miguel:** _____

**Rosa:** Encantada.

**Miguel:** _____

**Rosa:** ¿Quién es tu amigo?

**Miguel:** _____

**Rosa:** ¡Adiós!

**Miguel:** _____

**3** Practice introducing yourself to four of your classmates, then write their names below.

    **1.** Se llama _____

    **2.** Se llama _____

    **3.** Se llama _____

    **4.** Se llama _____

LECCIÓN PRELIMINAR

Back to School Resources

## ¡Mucho gusto! *Práctica B*

| ¡AVANZA! | **Goal:** Practice making introductions. |
| --- | --- |

**1** Draw a line through the response that doesn't belong.

1. ¿Quién es?
   a. Es señorita Machado.
   b. Señorita Machado quien es.

2. Me llamo Diana.
   a. El gusto es mío.
   b. Mucho gusto.

3. Me llamo Ana. ¿Y tú? ¿Cómo te llamas?
   a. Te llamas Miguel.
   b. Me llamo Miguel.

4. Te presento a Esteban.
   a. Encantado.
   b. Igualmente.

5. Mucho gusto.
   a. El gusto es mío.
   b. Perdón.

**2** Write the appropriate responses.

1. ¿Cómo te llamas? _____

2. Mucho gusto. _____

3. ¿Quién es? _____

4. Encantada. _____

5. Te presento a Rosa. _____

**3** Sit with two other classmates. Classmate A should introduce classmate B to classmate C. Next, classmate B should introduce classmate C to classmate A. Finally, classmate C should introduce classmate A to classmate B.

Luis, te presento a Sara.

¡Hola, Sara! Encantado.

Igualmente.

LECCIÓN PRELIMINAR

Back to School Resources

# ¡Mucho gusto! *Práctica C*

*Level 1/1A* pp. 6–9

> **¡AVANZA!**  **Goal:**  Practice making introductions.

**1** Circle the best response.

1. Me llamo Ana. ¿Y tú? ¿Cómo te llamas?
   a. Te llamas Miguel.   b. Me llamo Miguel.   c. Es Miguel.

2. ¿Quién es?
   a. Me llamo señorita Machado.
   b. Es señorita Machado.
   c. Señorita Machado quien es.

3. Te presento a Esteban.
   a. Encantado.   b. Se llama Esteban.   c. ¿Cómo se llama?

4. Me llamo Diana.
   a. Te presento Diana.   b. El gusto es mío.   c. Mucho gusto.

5. ¿Cómo se llama?
   a. Se llama señor Ortega.   b. Te llamas señor Ortega.   c. ¿Quién es?

**2** Esteban and Clara meet for the first time. Write a short dialogue between them on the lines below.

Esteban: _____

Clara: _____

Esteban: _____

Clara: _____

Esteban: _____

Clara: _____

**3** Imagine it is your first day of class. Practice introducing yourself to your teacher and at least two other students. Make sure to use the appropriate formal and informal expressions, depending on whom you are speaking with.

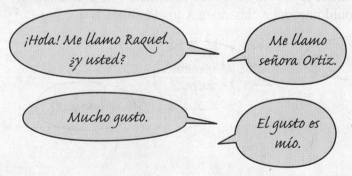

¡Hola! Me llamo Raquel. ¿y usted?

Me llamo señora Ortiz.

Mucho gusto.

El gusto es mío.

# El abecedario *Práctica A*

| ¡AVANZA! | **Goal:** Use the alphabet to spell words. |

**1** Underline the vowels and circle the letters that are unique to the Spanish alphabet in the following sentences. Then write the Spanish name of each letter in the sentence.

**1.** Hola. Me llamo Toño. ¿Cómo te llamas?

_____

_____

**2.** Buenos días, señora Carreras. Le presento a Guillermo.

_____

_____

**2** Make a list of at least three English words that begin with the following letters.

| ere | ele | de |
|-----|-----|-----|
|     |     |     |
|     |     |     |

**3** Read the sentences to a partner and have your partner copy down the letters to interpret what you are saying. Then, switch roles so you both have a chance to practice.

**1.** Hache-o-ele-a, ¿cu-u-é pe-a-ese-a?

_____

**2.** ¿Ce-ó-eme-o e-ese-te-á-ese?

_____

**3.** ¡Be-u-e-ene-a-ese te-a-ere-de-e-ese!

_____

**4.** ¡Hache-a-ese-te-a ele-u-e-ge-o!

_____

# El abecedario *Práctica B*

**Level 1/1A** pp. 10–11

> **¡AVANZA!**  **Goal:** Use the alphabet to spell words.

**1** Write your name and the names of your school, city, and state. Then write out how to spell each with Spanish letter names.

1. _____    _____

2. _____    _____

3. _____    _____

4. _____    _____

**2** Write out at least three English words that begin with each of the following letters.

| hache | a | jota | o | eme |
|-------|---|------|---|-----|
|       |   |      |   |     |
|       |   |      |   |     |
|       |   |      |   |     |
|       |   |      |   |     |

**3** Ask a partner to spell out three of his or her favorite movies. Write the names on the lines below.

**Favorite movies:**

_____

_____

## El abecedario *Práctica C*

> **¡AVANZA!**  **Goal:**  Use the alphabet to spell words.

**1** Use letters to rewrite the sentences that are written out in words.

   **1.** Te-e pe-ere-e-ese-e-ene-te-o a Eme-a-ere-í-a Jota-o-s-e.

   _____

   **2.** Hache-a-ese-te-a elé-u-e-ge-o, ese-e-eñe-o-ere Zeta-u-eñe-i-ge-a.

   _____

**2** Rewrite the sentences spelling out the name of each letter.

   **1.** Buenas tardes, Alex. ¿Qué tal?

   _____

   **2.** Hasta mañana, señora Rodríguez.

   _____

**3** Fill in the chart with at least four words that contain the following letters.

| eñe | erre | efe | u |
|-----|------|-----|---|
|     |      |     |   |
|     |      |     |   |
|     |      |     |   |
|     |      |     |   |

**4** Ask a partner to spell out the name of his or her favorite movie, song, food, and sport. Write the answers on the lines below.

**Favorite movie** _____

**Favorite song** _____

**Favorite food** _____

**Favorite sport** _____

# ¿De dónde eres? *Práctica A*

**¡AVANZA!**  **Goal:** Talk about Spanish-speaking countries and where people are from.

**1** Circle the answer that describes where the following people are from.

**1.** Eres de Colombia.
  **a.** You are from a Central American country.
  **b.** You are from a European country.
  **c.** You are from a South American Country.

**2.** Teresa es de Filipinas, Andrés es de Guam y Manuel es de Guinea Ecuatorial.
  **a.** They are from countries where Spanish is spoken, but not as an official language.
  **b.** They are from countries where Spanish is the native language.
  **c.** They are from countries that do not speak Spanish.

**3.** Elena es de Perú, Pedro es de Paraguay y Emilia es de Argentina.
  **a.** They are from Caribbean countries.
  **b.** They are from countries that border Brazil.
  **c.** They are from countries where Portuguese is the native language.

**2** Write the names of the countries not labeled on the map.

  **1.** _____
  **2.** _____
  **3.** _____
  **4.** _____

**3** Ask a partner where he or she is from, then switch roles and have your partner ask you. Use the countries listed below to answer.

| Estudiante 1 | Estudiante 2 |
| --- | --- |
| ¿De dónde eres? | Soy de:  Bolivia  República Dominicana  Honduras |
| Soy de:  Panamá  México  Argentina | ¿De dónde eres? |

# ¿De dónde eres? *Práctica B*

> **¡AVANZA!**    **Goal:**  Talk about Spanish-speaking countries and where people are from.

**1** Place a check next to the people who are from Spanish-speaking countries, then write a *1* next to those who speak Spanish as their official language and a *2* next to those who may speak Spanish as a second language.

☐ Guillermo es de Guam. _____

☐ Alejandro es de Paraguay. _____

☐ Sandra es de Guinea Ecuatorial. _____

☐ Cristina es de Honduras. _____

☐ Roberto es de Estados Unidos. _____

☐ Natalia es de Filipinas. _____

☐ Marta es de la República Dominicana. _____

☐ Jaime es de Venezuela. _____

☐ Luisa es de Perú. _____

**2** Write the names of the countries not labeled on the map.

1. _____

2. _____

3. _____

4. _____

5. _____

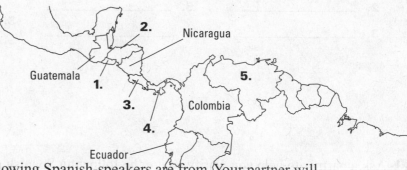

**3** Ask a partner where the following Spanish-speakers are from. Your partner will answer with the country listed.

**Modelo:**    ¿De dónde es Samuel?    *Es de Perú.*

| Estudiante 1 | Estudiante 2 |
|---|---|
| 1. Samuel | 1. Samuel ⟶ Perú |
| 2. Luis | 2. Luis ⟶ Puerto Rico |
| 3. Celia | 3. Celia ⟶ Nicaragua |
| 4. Pedro | 4. Pedro ⟶ México |
| 5. Ana | 5. Ana ⟶ Uruguay |
| 6. Marisol | 6. Marisol ⟶ Chile |

## ¿De dónde eres? *Práctica C*

> ¡AVANZA!  **Goal:**  Talk about Spanish-speaking countries and where people are from.

**1** Cross out the names of countries that don't belong in the categories; then write the names of the countries that do belong.

| Central American Spanish-Speaking Countries | South American Spanish-Speaking Countries | |
|---|---|---|
| Honduras | Chile | _____ |
| Colombia | Argentina | |
| Guatemala | Ecuador | |
| El Salvador | República Dominicana | _____ |
| Venezuela | Uruguay | |
| Panamá | Colombia | |
| | Perú | |
| _____ | Filipinas | |
| | México | |
| _____ | | |

**2** Identify the countries not labeled on the map.

1. _____    4. _____

2. _____    5. _____

3. _____    6. _____

Bolivia

Chile

**3** Ask a partner to help you clarify where the following Spanish speakers are from. Follow the model.

| Estudiante 1 | Estudiante 2 |
|---|---|
| **Modelo:** *¿Samuel es de Argentina?* | *No, Samuel es de Perú.* |
| 1. Samuel ⟶ Argentina | 1. Samuel ⟶ Perú |
| 2. Luis ⟶ Costa Rica | 2. Luis ⟶ Puerto Rico |
| 3. Celia ⟶ Honduras | 3. Celia ⟶ Nicaragua |
| 4. Pedro ⟶ España | 4. Pedro ⟶ México |
| 5. Ana ⟶ Cuba | 5. Ana ⟶ Uruguay |
| 6. Marisol ⟶ Paraguay | 6. Marisol ⟶ Chile |

# Mi número de teléfono *Práctica A*

> **¡AVANZA!** **Goal:** Practice using numbers one through ten and using phone numbers.

**1** Write in words the numbers missing in each sequence.

  **1.** cinco / cuatro / dos / uno / cero _____

  **2.** uno / tres / siete / nueve _____

  **3.** tres / cuatro / cinco / siete / ocho _____

  **4.** dos / cuatro / seis / diez _____

  **5.** diez / nueve / ocho / seis / cinco _____

**2** Use the words **más** (+) and **menos** (−) to write out the following math problems in words, then complete them by writing the correct answer.

  **1.** $3 + 2 = $ _____

  **2.** $10 - 3 = $ _____

  **3.** $7 - 1 = $ _____

  **4.** $6 + 3 = $ _____

  **5.** $2 + 5 = $ _____

**3** Make up a fake telephone number. Then, ask a partner: **¿Cuál es tu número de teléfono?** Switch roles and have your partner ask you. Next, ask your teacher: **¿Cuál es su número de teléfono?** Switch roles and have your teacher ask you. Write their fake numbers below.

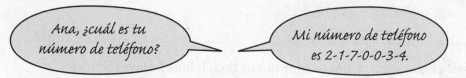

> Ana, ¿cuál es tu número de teléfono?

> Mi número de teléfono es 2-1-7-0-0-3-4.

  **1.** El número de teléfono de _____ es _____ .

  **2.** El número de teléfono de _____ es _____ .

## Mi número de teléfono *Práctica B*

| ¡AVANZA! | **Goal:** Practice using numbers one through ten and using phone numbers. |

**1** Write the numerals that correctly complete the math problems.

1. Dos más dos más tres = _____

2. Ocho menos uno menos dos = _____

3. Diez menos siete menos uno = _____

4. Uno más tres más dos = _____

5. Siete menos tres menos uno = _____

> más: +
>
> menos: −

**2** Write the numerals that correspond with the numbers written in words.

1. El número de teléfono de Carlos es cuatro-uno-seis-seis-siete-cero-dos.
   What is Carlos's telephone number?

   _____

2. El número de teléfono de Josefina es cinco-tres-uno-cero-nueve-ocho-nueve.
   What is Josefina's telephone number?

   _____

3. El número de teléfono de Sara es nueve-nueve-uno-dos-seis-cuatro-nueve.
   What is Sara's telephone number?

   _____

4. El número de teléfono de Jorge es uno-ocho-cero-seis-siete-uno-dos.
   What is Jorge's telephone number?

   _____

**3** Ask five of your classmates: **¿Cuál es tu número de teléfono?** Have them create a fake telephone number. Write their names and the telephone numbers they tell you on the chart below.

| NAME | TELEPHONE NUMBER |
|------|------------------|
|      |                  |
|      |                  |
|      |                  |
|      |                  |
|      |                  |

Nombre _____ Clase _____ Fecha _____

# Mi número de teléfono *Práctica C*

> **¡AVANZA!** **Goal:** Practice using numbers one through ten and using phone numbers.

**1** Write out the following telephone numbers in words in Spanish.

**1.** 5-7-6-9-2-9-8

_____

**2.** 6-0-1-2-3-1-5

_____

**3.** 9-2-7-0-6-8-4

_____

**4.** 3-1-5-0-0-8-7

_____

**2** Solve the following math problems to answer the questions with complete sentences. Use numerals in your answers.

**1. Julia:** Mi número de teléfono es tres menos uno – dos menos dos – siete más uno – diez menos cinco – cuatro más cuatro – ocho más uno – tres más seis.

What is Julia's phone number? _____

**2. Samuel:** Mi número de teléfono es tres más tres – cinco más dos – diez menos dos – ocho menos uno – diez menos seis – siete más dos – ocho menos cuatro.

What is Samuel's phone number? _____

**3** Read the following math problems to a partner. Your partner will then say aloud the correct answer. Switch roles so you both get a chance to practice solving the problems.

**1.** 2 + 3 = ?
**2.** 10 − 4 = ?
**3.** 3 + 3 = ?
**4.** 7 + 2 = ?
**5.** 8 − 5 = ?
**6.** 4 − 2 = ?
**7.** 9 + 1 = ?
**8.** 7 − 6 = ?

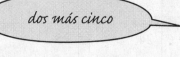
dos más cinco

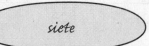
siete

**LECCIÓN PRELIMINAR**

**Back to School Resources**

## Los días de la semana *Práctica A*

> **¡AVANZA!**  **Goal:** Talk about the days of the week.

**1** Fill in the blanks with the correct day.

1. Hoy es viernes. Mañana es _____.
2. Hoy es miércoles. Mañana es _____.
3. Mañana es lunes. Hoy es _____.
4. Hoy es jueves. Mañana es _____.
5. Mañana es martes. Hoy es _____.
6. Mañana es jueves. Hoy es _____.
7. Hoy es lunes. Mañana es _____.

**2** Answer the following questions by writing the correct day(s) in Spanish.

1. What day is it today? _____
2. What day will it be tomorrow? _____
3. What are the days of the weekend? _____
4. Which days do you have Spanish class? _____
5. Which is your favorite day of the week? _____

**3** Point to a day on the calender and ask a partner the following question: **¿Que día es hoy?** He or she will use the calendar to answer you in a complete sentence. Take turns; each partner should ask about three days.

| Agosto | | | | | | |
|---|---|---|---|---|---|---|
| **L** | **M** | **M** | **J** | **V** | **S** | **D** |
| | 1 | 2 | 3 | 4 | 5 | 6 |
| 7 | 8 | 9 | 10 | 11 | 12 | 13 |
| 14 | 15 | 16 | 17 | 18 | 19 | 20 |
| 21 | 22 | 23 | 24 | 25 | 26 | 27 |
| 28 | 29 | 30 | 31 | | | |

# Los días de la semana *Práctica B*

> **¡AVANZA!**  **Goal:** Talk about the days of the week.

**1** Write the name of the correct day in Spanish.

| Agosto | | | | | | |
|---|---|---|---|---|---|---|
| **L** | **M** | **M** | **J** | **V** | **S** | **D** |
| | 1 | 2 | 3 | 4 | 5 | 6 |
| 7 | 8 | 9 | 10 | 11 | 12 | 13 |
| 14 | 15 | 16 | 17 | 18 | 19 | 20 |
| 21 | 22 | 23 | 24 | 25 | 26 | 27 |
| 28 | 29 | 30 | 31 | | | |

1. August 23 _____

2. August 12 _____

3. August 14 _____

4. August 4 _____

5. August 29 _____

6. August 6 _____

7. August 10 _____

**2** Name the day of the week that best answers each question.

1. ¿Qué día es hoy? _____

2. ¿Qué día es mañana? _____

3. ¿Qué día es después de (*after*) lunes? _____

4. ¿Qué día es antes de (*before*) viernes? _____

**3** Ask a partner the following questions. Write down your partner's answers on the lines below.

1. ¿Qué día es hoy?        —Hoy es _____ .

2. ¿Qué día es mañana?   —Mañana es _____ .

3. ¿Hoy es lunes?        —No or Sí, hoy es _____ .

4. ¿Mañana es sábado?   —No or Sí, mañana es _____ .

# Los días de la semana *Práctica C*

**¡AVANZA!** **Goal:** Talk about the days of the week.

**1** Fill in the blanks with the word **hoy** or **mañana** to describe the relationship between the following pairs of days.

1. _____ es viernes. _____ es sábado.
2. _____ es miércoles. _____ es jueves.
3. _____ es lunes. _____ es domingo.
4. _____ es jueves. _____ es viernes.
5. _____ es martes. _____ es lunes.
6. _____ es jueves. _____ es miércoles.
7. _____ es lunes. _____ es martes.

**2** Answer the following questions about the days of the week in complete sentences.

1. ¿Qué día es hoy? _____
2. ¿Qué día es mañana? _____
3. ¿Hoy es sábado? _____
4. ¿Mañana es domingo? _____
5. ¿Hoy es miércoles? _____

**3** Ask a partner the following questions; then write your partner's answers on the lines below.

1. ¿Qué día es mañana?
   _____
2. ¿Qué día es hoy?
   _____
3. ¿Mañana es martes?
   _____
4. ¿Hoy es lunes?
   _____
5. ¿Hoy es viernes?
   _____

# ¿Qué tiempo hace? *Práctica A*

> **¡AVANZA!**  **Goal:**  Describe different kinds of weather.

**1** Match the pictures with their corresponding weather descriptions.

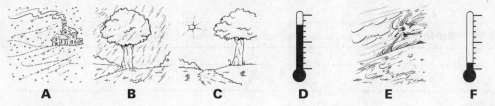

**A**      **B**      **C**      **D**      **E**      **F**

1. Hace viento. _____

2. Llueve. _____

3. Hace frío. _____

4. Hace sol. _____

5. Nieva. _____

6. Hace calor. _____

**2** Label each column with the kind of weather in which you would be most likely to wear the clothes listed.

| **Modelo:** *Nieva* | 1. _____ | 2. _____ | 3. _____ | 4. _____ |
|---|---|---|---|---|
| heavy coat gloves boots | sweater jeans wool cap | bathing suit sandals tank top | umbrella poncho rubber boots | sunglasses t-shirt sneakers |

**3** With a partner, take turns reading each other the following descriptions and guessing **¿Qué tiempo hace?** Write your answers on the lines provided.

1. You can go swimming in the ocean. You can walk in the park. You can eat lunch outside. ¿Qué tiempo hace?

   _____

2. You have to wear gloves and a hat as you make a snowman. ¿Qué tiempo hace?

   _____

3. You have to stay inside and read books or play games. ¿Qué tiempo hace?

   _____

4. You have to wear a sweater before you can go outside. ¿Qué tiempo hace?

   _____

5. You have to wear sunglasses and stay in the shade. ¿Qué tiempo hace?

   _____

# ¿Qué tiempo hace? *Práctica B*

> **¡AVANZA!**   **Goal:**   Describe different kinds of weather.

**1** List in Spanish the types of weather conditions that you might expect in the following seasons.

| Spring | Summer |
|---|---|
| _____ | _____ |
| _____ | _____ |
| _____ | _____ |

| Fall | Winter |
|---|---|
| _____ | _____ |
| _____ | _____ |
| _____ | _____ |

**2** List in Spanish the items of clothing you would most likely wear during the following weather conditions.

| Hace frío | Llueve | Hace calor |
|---|---|---|
|  |  |  |
|  |  |  |
|  |  |  |

**3** Ask a partner the following questions about the weather.

1. ¿Qué tiempo hace hoy?
2. ¿Qué tiempo hace en Cuba?
3. ¿Qué tiempo hace en Antártica?
4. ¿Qué tiempo hace en Chicago?

# ¿Qué tiempo hace? *Práctica C*

| ¡AVANZA! | **Goal:** Describe different kinds of weather. |
|---|---|

**1** Write the corresponding weather description for each illustration in a complete sentence.

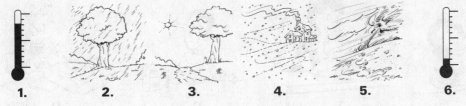

**1.** **2.** **3.** **4.** **5.** **6.**

1. _____
2. _____
3. _____
4. _____
5. _____
6. _____

**2** Use weather expressions to answer the following questions in complete sentences.

**1.** ¿Qué tiempo hace en el invierno (*the winter*)?

_____

**2.** ¿Qué tiempo hace en el verano (*the summer*)?

_____

**3.** ¿Qué tiempo hace donde vives tú (*where you live*)?

_____

**3** Ask a partner the following questions about what they do during different types of weather. Write the answers on the lines provided.

**1.** ¿Qué haces cuando llueve?

_____

**2.** ¿Qué haces cuando nieva?

_____

**3.** ¿Qué haces cuando hace calor?

_____

**4.** ¿Qué haces cuando hace frío?

_____

# En la clase *Práctica A*

| ¡AVANZA! | **Goal:** Practice using classroom instructions. |

**1** Match the classroom instructions with the illustrations that best correspond to them.

**A.**        **B.**        **C.**        **D.**

1. Cierren los libros. _____

2. Levanten la mano. _____

3. Saquen una hoja de papel. _____

4. Escucha. _____

**2** Use Spanish classroom instructions to tell the following stubborn students what to do.

**Modelo:**   Enrique doesn't want to read the book.   *Enrique, lee el libro.*

1. Maria does not want to ask questions. _____

2. Pablo and Ramón do not want to sit down. _____

3. Lupe doesn't want to listen. _____

4. Anita and Marcos do not want to open their book. _____

5. Samuel doesn't want to answer questions. _____

**3** Sit with two or three of your classmates. Take turns giving the other students instructions that they must act out.

1. Abran los libros.

2. Cierren los libros.

3. Levanten la mano.

4. Levántense.

5. Siéntense.

6. Escuchen.

7. Escriban.

8. Lean.

9. Saquen una hoja de papel.

# En la clase *Práctica B*

> **¡AVANZA!**   **Goal:**   Practice using classroom instructions.

**1** Draw lines to connect the questions with their logical responses.

1. ¿Cómo se dice *book* en español?
2. ¿Qué quiere decir **maestro**?
3. ¿Tienen preguntas?
4. ¿Cómo se escribe **español**?

a. Se escribe e-ese-pe-a-eñe-o-ele.
b. Se dice **libro**.
c. Sí, ¿cómo se dice *thank you*?
d. Quiere decir *teacher*.

**2** Write down the classroom instructions that the students in each picture are responding to.

1.    2.    3.    4.    5.

1. _____
2. _____
3. _____
4. _____
5. _____

**3** Ask a fellow student the following questions. He or she should answer you in a complete sentence. Write the answers on the lines provided.

1. ¿Cómo se escribe tu nombre?

_____

2. ¿Cómo se dice *It's raining*?

_____

# En la clase *Práctica C*

┌─────────────────────────────────────────────────────────────────┐
│  ¡AVANZA!     **Goal:**  Practice using classroom instructions.   │
└─────────────────────────────────────────────────────────────────┘

**1** Write the instructions you would give to your classmates in the following situations.

1. It's time to start class. _____

2. The students have to take notes. _____

3. The students have to read their textbook. _____

4. The students have many questions. _____

5. The class has ended. _____

**2** Respond in complete sentences to the following, using words and expressions from this lesson.

1. ¿Cómo se dice *question* en español?

   _____

2. ¿Qué quiere decir *¡Avanza!*?

   _____

3. ¿Cómo se escribe tu nombre?

   _____

4. ¿Qué dices cuando tu maestro(a) habla muy rápidamente (*speaks very quickly*)?

   _____

5. Muchas gracias.

   _____

**3** Sit with two or more of your classmates. Each student takes a turn acting out the classroom instructions while the remaining students try to guess which command is being enacted. The first student to guess and say the correct command aloud is the next to act out a different classroom instruction. Try not to use the same instructions more than once!

Copyright © by McDougal Littell, a division of Houghton Mifflin Company.

# Back to School Resources Answer Key

## HOLA, ¿QUÉ TAL?

*PRÁCTICA A* p. 1

**1**

1. c     2. b
3. a     4. b

**2**

1. Qué     2. Buenos     3. está
4. Buenas, tú     5. bien

**3** Answers will vary.

*PRÁCTICA B* p. 2

**1**

1. underline **Muy bien, ¿y tú?**
2. underline **Hasta mañana, Esteban.**
3. underline **Muy bien, gracias.**
4. underline **¿Cómo estás?**

**2**

1. Answers will vary. Possible: Muy bien, ¿y tú?
2. Answers may vary. Possible: Hasta mañana, señora.
3. Answers may vary. Possible: Hasta luego, Ana.
4. Answers may vary. Possible: ¿Cómo estás, Ana?

**3** Answers will vary.

*PRÁCTICA C* p. 3

**1**

1. circle **Buenos** and **está**
2. circle **días** and **tal**
3. circle **luego**
4. circle **Cómo** and **tú**
5. circle **menos** and **tú**
6. circle **Cómo** and **usted**

**2** Answers will vary.

**3** Answers will vary.

## ¡MUCHO GUSTO!

*PRÁCTICA A* p. 4

**1**

1. d     2. b     3. e
4. a     5. c

**2**

Me llamo Miguel., Igualmente., Possible: Es Juan., Possible: Hasta luego.

**3** Answers will vary.

*PRÁCTICA B* p. 5

**1**

1. a     2. b     3. b
4. a     5. a

**2**

1. Me llamo...
2. El gusto es mío.
3. Es...
4. Igualmente
5. Mucho gusto/Encantado.

**3** Answers will vary.

*PRÁCTICA C* p. 6

**1**

1. b     2. b     3. a
4. c     5. a

**2** Answers will vary.
Possible dialogue: **Esteban:** Hola. Me llamo Esteban, ¿y tú?, **Clara:** Hola, Esteban. Me llamo Clara., **Esteban:** Mucho gusto., **Clara:** El gusto es mío., **Esteban:** ¡Adiós, Clara!, **Clara:** Hasta luego, Esteban.

**3** Answers will vary.

LECCIÓN PRELIMINAR

Back to School Resources Answer Key

Copyright © by McDougal Littell, a division of Houghton Mifflin Company.

¡Avancemos! 1
Unit Resource Book

Lección preliminar
Back to School Resources Answer Key     25

# Back to School Resources Answer Key

## EL ABECEDARIO

*PRÁCTICA A* p. 7

1. circle ñ and ll. Hache-o-ele-a. Eme-e ele-ele-a-eme-o Te-o-ñ-o. ¿Ce-o-eme-o te-e ele-ele-a-eme-a-ese?

2. circle ñ, ll and rr. Be-u-e-ene-o-ese de-i-a-ese, ese-e-eñe-o-ere-a Ce-a-erre-e-ere-a-ese. Ele-e pe-ere-e-ese-e-ene-te-o a Ge-u-i-ele-ele-e-ere-eme-o.

❷ Answers will vary.

❸

1. Hola, ¿qué pasa?
2. ¿Cómo estás?
3. ¡Buenas tardes!
4. ¡Hasta luego!

*PRÁCTICA B* p. 8

❶ Answers will vary.
Example answer. Claire: ce-ele-a-i-ere-e, etc.

❷ Answers will vary.

❸ Answers will vary.

*PRÁCTICA C* p. 9

❶

1. Te presento a María Jose.
2. Hasta luego, señor Zuñiga.

❷

1. Be-u-e-ene-a-ese te-a-ere-de-e-s, A-ele-e-equis. ¿Cu-u-e te-a-ele?
2. Hache-a-ese-te-a eme-a-eñe-a-ene-a, ese-e-eñe-o-ere-a Ere-o-de-ere-i-ge-u-e-zeta.

❸ Answers will vary.

❹ Answers will vary.

## ¿DE DÓNDE ERES?

*PRÁCTICA A* p. 10

1. c    2. a    3. b

❷

1. Guatemala    2. El Salvador
3. Nicaragua    4. Panamá

❸ Answers will vary.

*PRÁCTICA B* p. 11

❶

**Guam (2), Paraguay (1), Guinea Ecuatorial (2), Honduras (1), Estados Unidos (2), Filipinas (2), República Dominicana (1), Venezuela (1), Perú (1).**

❷

1. El Salvador    2. Honduras
3. Costa Rica    4. Panamá
5. Venezuela

❸ Answers will vary.

*PRÁCTICA C* p. 12

❶

**Central America:** cross out Colombia and Venezuela, replace with Costa Rica and Nicaragua **South America:** cross out República Dominicana, Filipinas and México, replace with Venezuela, Bolivia and Paraguay

❷

1. Venezuela
2. Ecuador
3. Perú
4. Paraguay
5. Argentina
6. Uruguay

❸ Answers will vary.

# Back to School Resources Answer Key

## MI NÚMERO DE TELÉFONO

*PRÁCTICA A* p. 13

**1**

1. tres   2. cinco   3. seis
4. ocho   5. siete

**2**

1. tres más dos son cinco
2. diez menos tres son siete
3. siete menos uno son seis
4. seis más tres son nueve
5. dos más cinco son siete

**3** Answers will vary.

*PRÁCTICA B* p. 14

**1**

1. 7   2. 5   3. 2
4. 6   5. 3

**2**

1. Su número de teléfono es 4-1-6-6-7-0-2.
2. Su número de teléfono es 5-3-1-0-9-8-9.
3. Su número de teléfono es 9-9-1-2-6-4-9.
4. Su número de teléfono es 1-8-0-6-7-1-2.

**3** Answers will vary.

*PRÁCTICA C* p. 15

**1**

1. cinco-siete-seis-nueve-dos-nueve-ocho
2. sies-cero-uno-dos-tres-uno-cinco
3. nueve-dos-siete-cero-seis-ocho-cuatro
4. tres-uno-cinco-cero-cero-ocho-siete

**2**

1. El número de teléfono de Julia es 2-0-8-5-8-9-9.
2. El número de teléfono de Samuél es 6-7-8-7-4-9-4.

**3** Answers will vary.

## LOS DÍAS DE LA SEMANA

*PRÁCTICA A* p. 16

**1**

1. sábado
2. jueves
3. domingo
4. viernes
5. lunes
6. miércoles
7. martes

**2** Answers will vary.

**3** Answers will vary.

*PRÁCTICA B* p. 17

**1**

1. miércoles
2. sábado
3. lunes
4. viernes
5. martes
6. domingo
7. jueves

**2** Answers will vary.

**3** Answers will vary.

*PRÁCTICA C* p. 18

**1**

1. Hoy, Mañana
2. Hoy, Mañana
3. Mañana, Hoy
4. Hoy, Mañana
5. Mañana, Hoy
6. Mañana, Hoy,
7. Hoy, Mañana

**2** Answers will vary.

**3** Answers will vary.

LECCIÓN PRELIMINAR

Back to School Resources Answer Key

Copyright © by McDougal Littell, a division of Houghton Mifflin Company.

# Back to School Resources Answer Key

## ¿QUÉ TIEMPO HACE?

*PRÁCTICA A* p. 19

**1**

| | | | |
|---|---|---|---|
| 1. E | | 2. B | |
| 3. F | | 4. C | |
| 5. A | | 6. D | |

**2**

**Column 1:** Hace frío, **Column 2:** Hace calor, **Column 3:** Llueve, **Column 4:** Hace sol.

**3** Answers will vary.

*PRÁCTICA B* p. 20

**1** Answers will vary.

**2** Answers will vary.

**3** Answers will vary.

*PRÁCTICA C* p. 21

**1**

1. Hace calor.
2. Llueve.
3. Hace sol.
4. Nieva.
5. Hace viento.
6. Hace frío.

**2** Answers may vary. Possible:

1. Donde vivo yo hace frío en el invierno.
2. Donde vivo yo, hace calor en el verano.
3. Answers will vary.

**3** Answers will vary.

## EN LA CLASE

*PRÁCTICA A* p. 22

**1**

| | | | |
|---|---|---|---|
| 1. B | | 2. A | |
| 3. D | | 4. C | |

**2** Answers will vary.

**3** Answers will vary.

*PRÁCTICA B* p. 23

**1**

| | | | |
|---|---|---|---|
| 1. b | | 2. d | |
| 3. c | | 4. a | |

**2**

1. siéntense
2. levanten la mano
3. lee el libro
4. abran los libros
5. pregúntale a otro estudiante

**3** Answers will vary.

*PRÁCTICA C* p. 24

**1** Answers will vary. Possible:

1. Siéntense.
2. Saquen una hoja de papel.
3. Abran los libros.
4. Levanten la mano.
5. Cierren los libros.

**2** Answers will vary.

**3** Answers will vary.

Copyright © by McDougal Littell, a division of Houghton Mifflin Company.

# Did You Get It? *Presentación de vocabulario*

> **¡AVANZA!**    **Goal:**  Talk about activities.

## Personal Characteristics

• Different types of people like to do different things.

| | |
|---|---|
| *The musical type* | **escuchar música** *(to listen to music)* |
| | **tocar la guitarra** *(to play the guitar)* |
| *The friendly type* | **hablar por teléfono** *(to talk on the telephone)* |
| | **escribir correos electrónicos** *(to write e–mails)* |
| | **comprar** *(to go shopping)* |
| *The serious type* | **hacer la tarea** *(to do homework)* |
| | **leer un libro** *(to read a book)* |
| | **estudiar** *(to study)* |
| *The quiet type* | **pasear** *(to take a walk)* |
| | **descansar** *(to rest)* |
| | **mirar la televisión** *(to watch television)* |
| | **dibujar** *(to draw)* |
| *The athletic type* | **correr** *(to run)* |
| | **jugar al fútbol** *(to play soccer)* |
| | **montar en bicicleta** *(to ride a bike)* |
| | **andar en patineta** *(to skateboard)* |

• Here are ways to talk about what you and your friends like to do.

Say what you like to do:    **Me gusta comer pizza.** *(I like to eat pizza.)*

**Me gusta beber jugo.** *(I like to drink juice.)*

Ask what a friend likes to do:    **¿Qué actividad te gusta hacer?**
*(What activity do you like to do?)*

**¿Te gusta preparar la comida?**
*(Do you like to prepare food?)*

• Read this conversation between you and a friend.

You:  **¿Qué te gusta hacer?** *(What do you like to do?)*

Friend:  **Me gusta comer papas fritas.** *(I like to eat French fries.)*

You:  **¿Te gusta comer fruta?** *(Do you like to eat fruit?)*

Friend:  **Me gusta más comer galletas y helado.** *(I like to eat cookies and ice cream more.)*

# Did You Get It? *Práctica de vocabulario*

**¡AVANZA!**  **Goal:** Talk about activities.

**1** Which activity do you associate with each type of person?

**1.** a fan of hard rock

preparar la comida　　escuchar música　　andar en bicicleta

**2.** a good student

estudiar　　correr　　mirar la televisión

**3.** an athlete

descansar　　andar en bicicleta　　leer un libro

**4.** a sociable person

hacer la tarea　　pasar un rato con amigos　　beber un refresco

**5.** a person following a healthy diet

mirar la televisión　　comprar papas fritas　　comer fruta

**2** Which activity do you usually do . . .

**1.** . . . at dinner time?

comer papas fritas　　descansar　　jugar al fútbol

**2.** . . . in school?

descansar　　estudiar　　montar en bicicleta

**3.** . . . outdoors?

escribir correos electrónicos　　pasear　　mirar la televisión

**4.** . . . in the kitchen?

preparar la comida　　practicar los deportes　　andar en patineta

**5.** . . . on the soccer field?

jugar al fútbol　　escribir correos electrónicos　　comprar jugo

**6.** . . . at the computer?

descansar　　preparar la comida　　escribir correos electrónicos

UNIDAD 1 Lección 1
Reteaching and Practice

**3** **¿Qué te gusta hacer?** *(What do you like to do?)* Use the expression **Me gusta** *(I like)* followed by the activity shown to answer the question. One is done for you.

1.  2.  3.  4.  5.  6.

1. _Me gusta hablar por teléfono._

2. _____

3. _____

4. _____

5. _____

6. _____

**4** Which do you like better? Use **Me gusta más** *(I like _____ better)*.

1. ¿Te gusta más hacer la tarea o mirar la televisión?

_____

2. ¿Te gusta más beber agua o beber un refresco?

_____

3. ¿Te gusta más estudiar o pasar un rato con los amigos?

_____

4. ¿Te gusta más comer pizza o comer papas fritas?

_____

5. ¿Te gusta más escribir correos electrónicos o hacer la tarea?

_____

**5** Write a complete sentence naming three activities you like to do. Start your sentence with the expression **Me gusta**. Then read your sentence aloud.

_____

**6** Ask your friend what he or she likes to do. Write the question you asked and your friend's answer.

You: _____

Friend: _____

# Did You Get It? *Presentación de gramática*

| ¡AVANZA! | **Goal:** Learn about subject pronouns and how they are used with the verb **ser**. |
|---|---|

## Subject Pronouns

| | | |
|---|---|---|
| **Yo** soy Rolando. | *I am Rolando.* | |
| **Tú** eres Andrés. | *You are Andrés.* | |
| **Él** es Esteban. | *He is Esteban.* | *singular subject pronouns* |
| **Ella** es Mercedes. | *She is Mercedes.* | |
| **Usted** es el señor López. | *You are Mr. López.* | |

| | | |
|---|---|---|
| **Nosotros** somos José y Ana. | *We are José and Ana.* | |
| **Nosotras** somos Eva y Pilar. | *We are Eva and Pilar.* | |
| **Ellos** son Óscar y Felipe. | *They are Óscar and Felipe.* | *plural subject pronouns* |
| **Ellas** son Isabel y Luisa. | *They are Isabel and Luisa.* | |
| **Ustedes** son Marta y Álvaro. | *You are Marta and Álvaro.* | |

| | | |
|---|---|---|
| **Vosotros** sois Pepe y Arturo. | *You are Pepe and Arturo.* | *plural subject pronouns* |
| **Vosotras** sois Julia y Tina. | *You are Julia and Tina.* | *used only in Spain* |

**EXPLANATION:** *Subject pronouns* are used as the subject of a sentence. In general, they tell who is being described or who is doing the action. English has seven subject pronouns (the six above plus *it*). Spanish has twelve! (*It* is not expressed in Spanish.) In the sentences above, the subject pronouns are used with the verb **ser** (*to be*) to tell who people are.

## The Verb *ser* (to be)

| | | |
|---|---|---|
| Yo **soy** de Estados Unidos. | *I am from the United States.* | |
| Tú **eres** de Portugal. | *You are from Portugal.* | *singular forms of* **ser** |
| Él/Ella/Usted **es** de México. | *He/She/You is (are) from Mexico.* | |

| | | |
|---|---|---|
| Nosotros **somos** de Ecuador. | *We are from Ecuador.* | *plural forms of* **ser** |
| Ellos/Ellas/Ustedes **son** de Perú. | *They/You are from Peru.* | |

| | | |
|---|---|---|
| Vosotros (Vosotras) **sois** de España. | *You are from Spain.* | *plural forms of* **ser** *Sois used only in Spain* |

**EXPLANATION:** The verb **ser** means *to be*. The sentences in the first section use **ser** to tell *who* people are. The sentences in the second section use **ser** to say *where* they are from.

**UNIDAD 1 Lección 1**

**Reteaching and Practice**

# Did You Get It? *Práctica de gramática*

> **¡AVANZA!**  **Goal:** Learn about subject pronouns and how they are used with the verb **ser**.

**1** Which subject pronoun would you use if you were speaking *to* these people: **tú**, **usted**, or **ustedes**?

1. la maestra de español _____
2. tu amigo _____
3. dos amigos _____
4. el señor López _____
5. los padres de tu amigo _____
6. tus amigos José y Paco _____
7. el doctor García _____
8. tu mamá _____

**2** Which subject pronoun would you use if you were speaking *about* these people: **él**, **ella**, **nosotros**, **nosotras**, **ellos**, or **ellas**?

1. Andrés _____
2. el señor y la señora Valdés _____
3. tú y yo [Jorge] _____
4. Elena _____
5. Roberto, Luis y Álvaro _____
6. tu hermana _____
7. el abuelo _____
8. María y su mamá _____
9. Marielsa y yo [Ana] _____
10. el maestro _____

**3** Who are these people? Complete each sentence with the corresponding subject pronoun.

1. _____ eres Felipe.
2. _____ somos amigos.
3. _____ son maestros.
4. _____ es Luis.
5. _____ son Luisa y Elena.
6. _____ soy amiga de Ernesto.
7. _____ es la maestra de español.
8. _____ eres estudiante.
9. _____ es mi amigo.
10. _____ son estudiantes.

**UNIDAD 1 Lección 1** Reteaching and Practice

## 4 Where are these people from? Complete each sentence with the correct form of the verb **ser.**

1. Linda _____ de Estados Unidos.
2. Miguel y yo _____ de Argentina.
3. Tú _____ de Venezuela.
4. Ellos _____ de Puerto Rico.
5. Anita y usted _____ de España.
6. Yo _____ de Uruguay.
7. Él _____ de Perú.
8. Ustedes _____ de Cuba.
9. Pilar _____ de Ecuador.
10. Nosotros _____ de Nicaragua.

## 5 Use the information given to say who each person is and where each person is from. The first one is done for you.

1. yo / Carmen / la República Dominicana

   *Yo soy Carmen. Yo soy de la República Dominicana.*

2. nosotras / Lidia y Adela / Colombia

   _____

3. tú / Roque / El Salvador

   _____

4. ellos / Bárbara y Carlos / Uruguay

   _____

5. ustedes / los señores Tobar / Panamá

   _____

6. él / el maestro de español / España

   _____

## 6 Complete the conversation between José and Andrea using the correct form of **ser.**

**José:** ¡Hola! Yo _____ José.

**Andrea:** ¡Hola, José! Yo soy Andrea. Él _____ Miguel.

**José:** ¡Hola! ¿De dónde _____ ustedes?

**Andrea:** Nosotros _____ de Cuba. ¿De dónde _____ tú?

**José:** Yo _____ de Guatemala.

## 7 Write two sentences stating who you are and where you are from.

_____

_____

UNIDAD 1 Lección 1

Reteaching and Practice

# Did You Get It? *Presentación de gramática*

---

**¡AVANZA!**  **Goal:** Understand what an infinitive is and use infinitives with the verb **gustar**.

---

## The Infinitive

- An *infinitive* is the basic form of a verb. In English, most infinitives include the word *to*. Compare the following infinitive in Spanish and English:

| **Spanish** | **English** |
|---|---|
| le**er** | **to** read |

Infinitives have many uses. To talk about what people like to do, you simply use the infinitive after the verb **gustar**.

**Me gusta** leer. *(I like to read.)*  **Nos gusta** leer. *(We like to read.)*
**Te gusta** leer. *(You like to read.)*  **Os gusta** leer. *(You like to read.)*
**Le gusta** leer. *(He/She/You like(s) to read.)*  **Les gusta** leer. *(They/You like to read.)*

**EXPLANATION:** If you wonder why there are no subject pronouns (**yo, tú, él, ella, usted,** etc.) in the above sentences, it is because **gustar** literally means *to be pleasing*. When you say **Me gusta leer**, you are really saying, "To read is pleasing to me." To get the sentence correct in Spanish, you need to first rephrase the English sentence. Here's how it works:

| *I like to read.* | ⟶ | *To me it is pleasing to read.* | ⟶ | **Me gusta leer.** |
| *You like to read.* | ⟶ | *To you it is pleasing to read.* | ⟶ | **Te gusta leer.** |
| *He likes to read.* | ⟶ | *To him it is pleasing to read.* | ⟶ | **Le gusta leer.** |
| *We like to read.* | ⟶ | *To us it is pleasing to read.* | ⟶ | **Nos gusta leer.** |
| *You like to read.* | ⟶ | *To you it is pleasing to read.* | ⟶ | **Os gusta leer.** |
| *They like to read.* | ⟶ | *To them it is pleasing to read.* | ⟶ | **Les gusta leer.** |

- When you want to emphasize or identify the person who is pleased, you can add the corresponding noun or pronoun preceded by **a**:

    **A Sonia le gusta** leer.
    *Sonia likes to read. (To Sonia it is pleasing to read.)*

    **A ella le gusta** leer.
    *She likes to read. (To her it is pleasing to read.)*

- These are the *pronouns* that follow **a**:

| | |
|---|---|
| **A mí me gusta** correr. *(I)* | **A nosotros(as) nos gusta** correr. *(We)* |
| **A ti te gusta** correr. *(You)* | **A vosotros(as) os gusta** correr. *(You)* |
| **A usted le gusta** correr. *(You)* | **A ustedes les gusta** correr. *(You)* |
| **A él o ella le gusta** correr. *(He or She)* | **A ellos(as) les gusta** correr. *(They)* |

# Did You Get It? *Práctica de gramática*

**¡AVANZA!**    **Goal:**    Understand what an infinitive is and use infinitives with the verb **gustar**.

**❶** Match each English phrase with the corresponding Spanish phrase.

1. I like . . .          Les gusta...
2. They like . . .       Nos gusta...
3. He likes . . .        Me gusta...
4. We like . . .         Te gusta...
5. You like . . .        Le gusta...

**❷** Who likes what? Choose the correct English sentence.

1. Le gusta comer.
   a. I like to eat.
   b. We like to eat.
   c. He likes to eat.

2. Me gusta montar en bicicleta.
   a. He likes to ride a bicycle.
   b. I like to ride a bicycle.
   c. She likes to ride a bicycle.

3. Te gusta jugar al fútbol.
   a. We like to play soccer.
   b. He likes to play soccer.
   c. You like to play soccer.

4. Nos gusta leer.
   a. We like to read.
   b. They like to read.
   c. You like to read.

5. Les gusta estudiar.
   a. We like to study.
   b. He likes to study.
   c. They like to study.

6. Le gusta beber agua.
   a. He likes to drink water.
   b. They like to drink water.
   c. I like to drink water.

**❸** Choose one of the phrases to complete the sentences in Spanish.

| Les gusta | Me gusta | Le gusta | Nos gusta | Te gusta |
| --- | --- | --- | --- | --- |

1. She likes to watch television.
   _____ mirar la televisión.

2. We like to run.
   _____ correr.

3. You like to rest.
   _____ descansar.

4. I like to do homework.
   _____ hacer la tarea.

5. They like to play soccer.
   _____ jugar al fútbol.

6. He likes to drink water.
   _____ beber agua.

UNIDAD 1 Lección 1
Reteaching and Practice

**4** What do these people like to do? Answer each question using one of these pronoun phrases: **a mí**, **a ti**, **a él**, **a ella**, **a usted**, **a nosotros(as)**, **a vosotros(as)**, **a ellos(as)**, **a ustedes**.

1.

2.

3.

4.

5.

6.

7.

8.

**1.** ¿Qué le gusta hacer a Jorge?

_____

**2.** ¿Qué le gusta hacer a la señora Donadi?

_____

**3.** ¿Qué te gusta hacer a ti?

_____

**4.** ¿Qué me gusta hacer a mí? (**tú**)

_____

**5.** ¿Qué les gusta hacer a Leyla y a Ana?

_____

**6.** ¿Qué nos gusta hacer a Pedro y a mí?

_____

**7.** ¿Qué me gusta hacer a mí? (**usted**)

_____

**8.** ¿Qué nos gusta hacer a nosotros?

_____

UNIDAD 1 Lección 1    Reteaching and Practice

♻ **¿Recuerdas?**

## Weather Expressions

• Look at the following weather expressions in Spanish.

**Hace sol.** *(It's sunny.)*          **Hace calor.** *(It's hot.)*

**Hace viento.** *(It's windy.)*       **Hace frío.** *(It's cold.)*

**EXPLANATION:** For some weather expressions, use the verb **hace**.

• Now look at these weather expressions.

**Llueve.** *(It's raining.)*          **Nieva.** *(It's snowing.)*

**EXPLANATION:** Some weather expressions have their own verb.

___

**❶** Write a weather expression in Spanish to describe each picture.

1.          2.          3.          4.          5.          6.

1. _____          4. _____

2. _____          5. _____

3. _____          6. _____

**❷** What is the ideal weather for these activities?

1. skiing _____

2. going to the beach _____

3. going sailing _____

4. watching tv _____

5. drinking hot chocolate _____

6. taking a walk _____

UNIDAD 1 Lección 1

Reteaching and Practice

# Did You Get It? *Presentación de vocabulario*

> **¡AVANZA!**   **Goal:**   Describe yourself and your friends.

## Opposites Attract!

- Look at the pictures and study the words.

**alto(a)** *(tall)*

**grande** *(big)*

**trabajador(a)** *(hard worker)*

**bajo(a)** *(short)*

**pequeño(a)** *(small)*

**perezoso(a)** *(lazy)*

**serio(a)** *(serious)*

**organizado(a)** *(organized)*

**joven** *(young)*

**cómico(a)** *(funny)*

**desorganizado(a)**
*(unorganized)*

**viejo(a)** *(old)*

- Describe these people using the words above:

  **la mujer** *(woman)*     **el hombre** *(man)*     **la chica** *(girl)*     **el chico** *(boy)*

- These are other ways to describe people.

  La mujer es **bonita**. Tiene **pelo castaño**.     *(The woman is **pretty**. She has **brown hair**.)*
  El hombre es **guapo**. Tiene **pelo rubio**.     *(The man is **handsome**. He has **blonde hair**.)*
  La chica es **artística**. Es **pelirroja**.     *(The girl is **artistic**. She has **red hair**.)*
  El chico es **atlético**. Es **estudioso**.     *(The boy is **athletic**. He is **studious**.)*
  El chico no es **malo**. Es **bueno**.     *(The boy is not **bad**. He is **good**.)*

UNIDAD 1 Lección 2   Reteaching and Practice

# Did You Get It? *Práctica de vocabulario*

**¡AVANZA!**  **Goal:** Describe yourself and your friends.

**1** Match the English and Spanish words.

| | | |
|---|---|---|
| **1.** artistic | rubio |
| **2.** brunette | malo |
| **3.** pretty | estudioso |
| **4.** redhead | artístico |
| **5.** bad | pelo castaño |
| **6.** studious | bonito |
| **7.** athletic | pelirrojo |
| **8.** blonde | atlético |

**2** Which adjective would you use to describe each person?

**1.** likes to do homework

estudioso        cómico        guapo

**2.** likes to draw

malo        artístico        cómico

**3.** doesn't like to joke around

pelirroja        seria        perezosa

**4.** likes to play sports

viejo        desorganizado        atlético

**5.** likes to work

perezoso        joven        trabajador

**6.** doesn't like to tidy up

desorganizada        cómica        bonita

**3** Choose the word that means the opposite of the word given.

**1.** bajo

    alto                      grande                  viejo

**2.** grande

    perezoso               pequeño              bajo

**3.** serio

    organizado           trabajador         cómico

**4.** joven

    pequeño               viejo              estudioso

**5.** trabajador

    desorganizado        perezoso           alto

**4** Complete each sentence to describe each picture.

    **1.**              **2.**              **3.**              **4.**

**1.** La mujer es _____ .

**2.** El chico es _____ .

**3.** El hombre es _____ .

**4.** La chica es _____ .

**5** Write a sentence using at least two adjectives to describe each person.

**1.** *Your best friend* _____

**2.** *Your Spanish teacher* _____

**3.** *You!* _____

UNIDAD 1 Lección 2   Reteaching and Practice

# Did You Get It? *Presentación de gramática*

> **¡AVANZA!**  **Goal:**  Learn about definite and indefinite articles.

## Gender and Number

In Spanish, all nouns are either masculine or feminine. Like in English, all nouns are also singular or plural. Read the following sentences paying attention to the boldfaced letters.

| | | | |
|---|---|---|---|
| el libr**o** | *(the book)* | los libro**s** | *(the books)* |
| la chic**a** | *(the girl)* | las chica**s** | *(the girls)* |
| el hombr**e** | *(the man)* | los hombre**s** | *(the men)* |
| la muje**r** | *(the woman)* | las mujer**es** | *(the women)* |

**EXPLANATION:** Nouns ending in **-o** in Spanish are usually *masculine*. Nouns ending in **-a** are usually *feminine*. Some words do not end with **-o** or **-a**. To form the plural of a noun, add **-s** if it ends in a vowel. Add **-es** if it ends in a consonant.

## Definite Articles

Definite articles are used with nouns to indicate specific persons, places, or things. Read these sentences, paying special attention to the boldfaced words.

| | |
|---|---|
| **El** libro es bueno. | *(**The** book is good.)* |
| **La** mujer es alta. | *(**The** woman is tall.)* |
| **Los** libros son buenos. | *(**The** books are good.)* |
| **Las** mujeres son altas. | *(**The** women are tall.)* |

**EXPLANATION:** English has one definite article: *the*. Spanish has four: **el, la, los, las**. The definite article must agree in gender and number with the noun following it.

## Indefinite Articles

Indefinite articles are used with nouns to indicate *unspecific* persons, places, or things. Read these sentences, paying special attention to the boldfaced words.

| | |
|---|---|
| Es **un** artista. | *(He is **an** artist.)* |
| Es **una** mujer. | *(She is **a** woman.)* |
| Son **unos** correos electrónicos. | *(They are **some** emails.)* |
| Son **unas** mujeres. | *(They are **some** women.)* |

**EXPLANATION:** English has three indefinite articles: *a, an, some*. Spanish has four: **un, una, unos, unas**. Like definite articles, indefinite articles must agree in gender and number with the nouns following them.

# Did You Get It? *Práctica de gramática*

**¡AVANZA!**   **Goal:**   Learn about definite and indefinite articles.

**1** Write the correct definite article.

| el | la | los | las |
|---|---|---|---|

1. _____ amigo
2. _____ chicas
3. _____ maestros
4. _____ mujer
5. _____ hombre

6. _____ hombres
7. _____ personas
8. _____ amiga
9. _____ estudiante
10. _____ maestras

**2** Write the correct indefinite article.

| un | una | unos | unas |
|---|---|---|---|

1. _____ guitarra
2. _____ libros
3. _____ deporte
4. _____ correos electrónicos
5. _____ bicicleta

6. _____ teléfonos
7. _____ correo electrónico
8. _____ bicicletas
9. _____ libro
10. _____ televisión

**3** Write the following in Spanish.

1. a book _____
2. a skateboard _____
3. the woman _____
4. some girls _____
5. the television _____

6. some teachers _____
7. a female friend _____
8. some friends _____
9. the guitar _____
10. an ice cream _____

UNIDAD 1 Lección 2   Reteaching and Practice

**4** Complete the sentences with the correct indefinite article.

1. Es _____ pizza.
2. Son _____ helados.
3. Es _____ helado.
4. Es _____ fruta.
5. Son _____ papas fritas.
6. Es _____ refresco.

**5** Complete the sentences with the correct definite article.

1. Son _____ helados.
2. Son _____ refrescos.
3. Son _____ pizzas.
4. Es _____ jugo.
5. Es _____ fruta.
6. Son _____ papas fritas.

**6** Write the following in Spanish.

1. She is a woman. _____
2. They are some friends. _____
3. He is a friend. _____
4. They are some girls. _____
5. He is the student. _____
6. He is a man. _____

UNIDAD 1 Lección 2 — Reteaching and Practice

# Did You Get It? *Presentación de gramática*

 **Goal:** Use adjectives with nouns.

## Placement of Adjectives

*Adjectives* are words that describe *nouns*. Read the following phrases, paying attention to where the adjective in Spanish is placed in relation to the noun it is describing.

el chico **alto** *(the **tall** boy)*      los chicos **altos** *(the **tall** boys)*

la chica **alta** *(the **tall** girl)*      las chicas **altas** *(the **tall** girls)*

**EXPLANATION:** In English, the adjective almost always comes *before* the noun. In Spanish, the adjective usually comes *after* the noun.

## Agreement of Adjectives

Read the same expressions again, this time paying attention to the boldfaced letters.

el chic**o** alt**o** *(the tall boy)*      los chic**os** alt**os** *(the tall boys)*

la chic**a** alt**a** *(the tall girl)*      las chic**as** alt**as** *(the tall girls)*

**EXPLANATION:** In Spanish, adjectives must match the gender and number of the nouns they describe.

## Agreement of Adjectives Not Ending in *-o*

Read the following four sets of noun and adjective phrases. Pay attention to the boldfaced letters to see how the adjectives that do not end in **-o** match in gender and number.

1. el chic**o** inteligent**e** *(the intelligent boy)*
   la chic**a** inteligent**e** *(the intelligent girl)*

2. el chic**o** jove**n** *(the young boy)*
   la chic**a** jove**n** *(the young girl)*

3. el chic**o** trabajado**r** *(the hard-working boy)*
   la chic**a** trabajado**ra** *(the hard-working girl)*

4. los chic**os** trabajado**res** *(the hard-working boys)*
   las chic**as** trabajado**ras** *(the hard-working girls)*

**EXPLANATION:** Adjectives that end in **-e** match both genders. Many adjectives that end in a consonant, such as **-n**, match both genders. Some adjectives that end in a consonant add **-a** to form the feminine. To make an adjective plural, add **-es** if it ends in a consonant and add **-s** if it ends in a vowel.

# Did You Get It? *Práctica de gramática*

| ¡AVANZA! | **Goal:** Use adjectives with nouns. |
|---|---|

**1** Which adjective goes with each person?

1. un chico          alto          alta
2. una mujer         pequeño       pequeña
3. una persona       atlético      atlética
4. un hombre         perezoso      perezosa
5. una maestra       bonito        bonita

**2** Which adjective goes with these people?

1. unos señores      artísticos    artísticas
2. unos maestros     organizados   organizadas
3. unas señoras      serios        serias
4. unos amigos       simpáticos    simpáticas
5. unas estudiantes  estudiosos    estudiosas

**3** Write the opposite of the underlined adjective.

1. Ana no es seria. Es _____ .
2. José y Jorge no son altos. Son _____ .
3. Los señores García no son perezosos. Son _____ .
4. La maestra de español no es organizada. Es _____ .
5. La guitarra no es grande. Es _____ .
6. La comida no es mala. Es _____ .

**4** Help Juan tell Sandra about his friends by completing his e–mail.

| A: Sandra |
|---|
| DE: Juan |

Hola, Sandra:

¿Mis amigos? Todos son _____ (simpático). Mi amigo Alejandro es
_____ (inteligente) y _____ (guapo). Mi amiga Susana es
_____ (serio) y _____ (bonito). A Jorge y a Luisa les gusta
correr porque son muy _____ (atlético). A José Antonio le gusta dibujar. Él
es muy _____ (artístico). Nosotros somos _____ (estudioso) y
_____ (trabajador). Somos estudiantes muy _____ (bueno). ¿Y
tus amigos? ¿Cómo son?    –Juan

UNIDAD 1 Lección 2

Reteaching and Practice

**5** Write the correct form of an adjective from the box to complete each sentence. Use each adjective only once.

| | | | | |
|---|---|---|---|---|
| desorganizado | atlético | inteligente | grande | cómico |
| trabajador | guapo | malo | bajo | joven |

**1.**    **2.**    **3.**    **4.**    **5.**

**6.**    **7.**    **8.**    **9.**    **10.**

**1.** Julio es _____ .

**2.** José es _____ .

**3.** Ana y Luisa son _____ .

**4.** Antonio es _____ .

**5.** Nosotros somos _____ .

**6.** Las chicas son _____ .

**7.** Los amigos son _____ .

**8.** Félix es _____ .

**9.** Mini es _____ .

**10.** La chica es _____ .

**6** Use **ser** and one or more adjectives to describe the following people and pets.

**1.** Yo _____

**2.** Mi madre *(mother)* _____

**3.** Mi padre *(father)* _____

**4.** Mi mejor *(best)* amigo _____

**5.** Mi mejor amiga _____

**6.** Mis amigos y yo _____

**7.** Mi primo *(cousin)* Adán _____

**8.** Mi prima *(cousin)* Gloria _____

**9.** Mi perro *(dog)* Mota _____

**10.** Mi gata *(cat)* Divina _____

UNIDAD 1 Lección 2   Reteaching and Practice

 **¿Recuerdas?** *Snack Foods*

• Here are the Spanish names of some snack foods.

| | | | | | |
|---|---|---|---|---|---|
| **las galletas** | **las papas fritas** | **la pizza** | **el helado** | **el jugo** | **el agua** |

## Práctica

**1** Write the name of each snack food and drink in Spanish.

**1.**    **2.**    **3.**    **4.**    **5.**    **6.**

1. _____

2. _____

3. _____

4. _____

5. _____

6. _____

**2** What do you like to eat and drink . . .

1. . . . in the summer? _____

2. . . . in the morning? _____

3. . . . for dinner? _____

4. . . . in the winter? _____

5. . . . for dessert? _____

UNIDAD 1 Lección 2

Reteaching and Practice

## ¿Recuerdas?

### Gustar + an infinitive

- You can use the verb **gustar** and an infinitive to talk about things people like to do. For example:

  **Me gusta** correr. *(I like to run.)*          **Nos gusta** correr. *(We like to run.)*

  **Te gusta** correr. *(You like to run.)*        **Os gusta** correr. *(You like to run.)*

  **Le gusta** correr. *(He/She/You likes to run.)*   **Les gusta** correr. *(They/You like to run.)*

- When you want to emphasize or identify who likes to do something, add the corresponding noun or pronoun preceded by **a**:

  **A Marta le gusta** correr.          **A ella le gusta** correr.

  *Marta likes to run.*                 *She likes to run.*

- These are the *pronouns* that follow **a**.

  **A mí me gusta** correr. *(I)*          **A nosotros(as) nos gusta** correr. *(We)*

  **A ti te gusta** correr. *(You)*        **A vosotros(as) os gusta** correr. *(You)*

  **A usted le gusta** correr. *(You)*     **A ustedes les gusta** correr. *(You)*

  **A él o ella le gusta** correr. *(He or She)*   **A ellos(as) les gusta** correr. *(They)*

## Práctica

**1** Write these sentences in Spanish.

1. Juan likes to write emails. _____

2. Alex likes to study. _____

3. We like to drink water. _____

4. They like to play football. _____

5. I like to eat fruit. _____

6. My father likes to read. _____

7. You *(plural)* like to eat. _____

8. She likes to spend time with friends. _____

9. He likes to draw. _____

10. We like to rest. _____

## ♻ ¿Recuerdas?

Level 1 pp. 32–33
Level 1A pp. 32–34

### After-school Activities

• Here are some expressions for after-school activities.

**Indoor Activities**

**mirar la televisión**
*(to watch television)*

**preparar la comida**
*(to prepare food)*

**descansar**
*(to rest)*

**hacer la tarea**
*(to do homework)*

**escribir correos electrónicos**
*(to write e–mails)*

**estudiar**
*(to study)*

**Both**

**escuchar música**
*(to listen to music)*

**dibujar** *(to draw)*

**tocar la guitarra**
*(to play the guitar)*

**comer pizza** *(to eat pizza)*

**hablar por teléfono**
*(to talk on the phone)*

**pasar un rato con los amigos**
*(to spend time with friends)*

**practicar deportes** *(to play sports)*

**comprar** *(to go shopping)*

**leer un libro**
*(to read a book)*

**Outdoor Activities**

**montar en bicicleta**
*(to ride a bike)*

**andar en patineta**
*(to skateboard)*

**correr**
*(to run)*

**jugar al fútbol**
*(to play football)*

**pasear**
*(to take a walk)*

## Práctica

❶ What do you like to do most? Follow the model.

**Modelo:** ¿Qué actividad te gusta más, practicar deportes o pasear? *Me gusta más pasear.*

**1.** ¿Hablar por teléfono o escribir correos electrónicos? _____

**2.** ¿Leer o escribir? _____

**3.** ¿Escuchar música o mirar la televisión? _____

❷ What do the following people like to do?

**1.** Julio es atlético. Le gusta _____

**2.** Anita es artística. Le gusta _____

**3.** Susana es simpática. Le gusta _____

❸ Complete the sentence telling two activities that you like to do and two activities that you don't like to do.

Me gusta _____

No me gusta _____

# Did You Get It? Answer Key

## PRÁCTICA DE VOCABULARIO

PERSONAL CHARACTERISTICS pp. 30–31

**1**
1. escuchar música
2. estudiar
3. andar en bicicleta
4. pasar un rato con amigos
5. comer fruta

**2**
1. comer papas fritas
2. estudiar
3. pasear
4. preparar la comida
5. jugar al fútbol
6. escribir correos electrónicos

**3**
1. *Me gusta hablar por teléfono.*
2. Me gusta comer papas fritas.
3. Me gusta montar en bicicleta.
4. Me gusta escuchar música.
5. Me gusta preparar la comida.
6. Me gusta andar en patineta.

**4** Answers will vary.

**5** Answers will vary.

**6** Answers will vary.

## PRÁCTICA DE GRAMÁTICA

SUBJECT PRONOUNS p. 33

**1**
1. usted
2. tú
3. ustedes
4. usted
5. ustedes
6. ustedes
7. usted
8. tú

**2**
1. él
2. ellos
3. nosotros
4. ella
5. ellos
6. ella
7. él
8. ellas
9. nosotras
10. él

**3**
1. Tú
2. Nosotros
3. Ellos (Ustedes)
4. Él
5. Ellas
6. Yo
7. Ella
8. Tú
9. Usted (Él)
10. Ustedes (Ellos, Ellas)

THE VERB **SER** p. 34

**4**
1. es
2. somos
3. eres
4. son
5. son
6. soy
7. es
8. son
9. es
10. somos

**5**
1. *Yo soy Carmen. Yo soy de la República Dominicana.*
2. Nosotras somos Lidia y Adela. Nosotras somos de Colombia.
3. Tú eres Roque. Tú eres de El Salvador.
4. Ellos son Bárbara y Carlos. Ellos son de Uruguay.
5. Ustedes son los señores Tobar. Ustedes son de Panamá.
6. Él es el maestro de español. Él es de España.

**UNIDAD 1 Lección 1** Reteaching and Practice Answer Key

# Did You Get It? Answer Key

**6**

José: ¡Hola! Yo **[soy]** José.

Andrea: ¡Hola, José! Yo soy Andrea. Él **[es]** Miguel.

José: ¡Hola!¿De dónde **[son]** ustedes?

Andrea: Nosotros **[somos]** de Cuba. ¿De dónde **[eres]** tú?

José: Yo **[soy]** de Guatemala.

**7** Answers will vary.

## PRÁCTICA DE GRAMÁTICA

### THE INFINITIVE pp. 36–37

**1**

1. I like... Me gusta...
2. They like... Les gusta...
3. He likes... Le gusta...
4. We like... Nos gusta...
5. You like...Te gusta...

**2**

| | | |
|---|---|---|
| 1. c | 2. b | 3. c |
| 4. a | 5. c | 6. a |

**3**

1. Le gusta
2. Nos gusta
3. Te gusta
4. Me gusta
5. Les gusta
6. Le gusta

**4**

1. A él le gusta escribir correos electrónicos.
2. A ella le gusta leer un libro.
3. A mí me gusta montar en bicicleta.
4. A ti te gusta escuchar música.
5. A ellas les gusta mirar la televisión.
6. A ustedes les gusta comer helado.
7. A usted le gusta preparar la comida.
8. A ustedes les gusta hablar por teléfono.

## ¿RECUERDAS?

### WEATHER EXPRESSIONS p. 38

**1**

1. Hace sol.
2. Llueve.
3. Nieva.
4. Hace viento.
5. Hace calor.
6. Hace frío.

**2**

1. Nieva.
2. Hace sol. / Hace calor.
3. Hace viento.
4. Llueve.
5. Hace frío. / Nieva.
6. Hace sol.

# Did You Get It? Answer Key

## PRÁCTICA DE VOCABULARIO

OPPOSITES ATTRACT! pp. 40–41

**1**

1. artistic, artístico
2. brunette, pelo castaño
3. pretty, bonito
4. redhead, pelirrojo
5. bad, malo
6. studious, estudioso
7. athletic, atlético
8. blonde, rubio

**2**

1. estudioso
2. artístico
3. seria
4. atlético
5. trabajador
6. desorganizada

**3**

1. alto
2. pequeño
3. cómico
4. viejo
5. perezoso

**4**

1. vieja
2. desorganizado
3. cómico
4. perezosa

**5** Answers will vary.

# DidYou Get It? Answer Key

## PRÁCTICA DE GRAMÁTICA

GENDER, NUMBER, DEFINITE AND
INDEFINITE ARTICLES pp. 43–44

**1**

1. el
2. las
3. los
4. la
5. el
6. los
7. las
8. la
9. el / la
10. las

**2**

1. una
2. unos
3. un
4. unos
5. una
6. unos
7. un
8. unas
9. un
10. una

**3**

1. un libro
2. una patineta
3. la mujer
4. unas chicas
5. la televisión
6. unos maestros
7. una amiga
8. unos amigos
9. la guitarra
10. un helado

**4**

1. una
2. unos
3. un
4. una
5. unas
6. un

**5**

1. los
2. los
3. las
4. el
5. la
6. las

**6**

1. Es una mujer.
2. Son unos amigos.
3. Es un amigo.
4. Son unas chicas.
5. Es el estudiante.
6. Es un hombre.

## PRÁCTICA DE GRAMÁTICA

ADJECTIVES pp. 46–47

**1**

1. alto
2. pequeña
3. atlética
4. perezoso
5. bonita

**2**

1. artísticos
2. organizados
3. serias
4. simpáticos
5. estudiosas

# Did You Get It? Answer Key

**3**

1. cómica
2. bajos
3. trabajadores
4. desorganizada
5. pequeña
6. buena

**4**

¿Mis amigos? Todos son **simpáticos** (simpático). Mi amigo Alejandro es **inteligente** (inteligente) y **guapo** (guapo). Mi amiga Susana es **seria** (serio) y **bonita** (bonito). A Jorge y a Luisa les gusta correr porque son muy **atléticos** (atlético). A José Antonio le gusta dibujar. Él es muy **artístico** (artístico). Nosotros somos **estudiosos** (estudioso) y **trabajadores** (trabajador). Somos estudiantes muy **buenos** (bueno). ¿Y tus amigos? ¿Cómo son?

Juan

**5**

1. desorganizado
2. bajo
3. inteligentes
4. grande
5. cómicos
6. atléticas
7. trabajadores
8. malo
9. guapa / joven
10. joven / guapa

**6** Answers will vary.

 **¿RECUERDAS?**

Práctica p. 48
Snack Foods

**1**

1. el agua
2. el helado
3. las papas fritas
4. el jugo
5. las galletas
6. la pizza

**2** Answers will vary.

# Did You Get It? Answer Key

Práctica p. 49
**Gustar** + an infinitive

**❶**

1. A Juan le gusta escribir correos electrónicos.
2. A Alex le gusta estudiar.
3. A nosotros nos gusta beber agua. / Nos gusta beber agua.
4. A ellos les gusta jugar al fútbol. / Les gusta jugar al fútbol.
5. A mí me gusta comer fruta. / Me gusta comer fruta.
6. A mi padre le gusta leer.
7. A ustedes les gusta comer. / Les gusta comer.
8. A ella le gusta pasar un rato con los amigos. / Le gusta pasar un rato con los amigos.
9. A él le gusta dibujar. / Le gusta dibujar.
10. A nosotros nos gusta descansar. / Nos gusta descansar.

**¿RECUERDAS?**

Práctica p. 50
**After-school Activities**

**❶** Answers will vary.

**❷**

1. jugar al fútbol
2. dibujar
3. pasar un rato con los amigos

**❸** Answers will vary.

*UNIDAD 1 Lección 2*

*Reteaching and Practice Answer Key*

# Sopa de letras *Práctica de vocabulario*

Unscramble the following words from the **Vocabulario**, then find them in the word search below.

le eaohld _____        goju le _____

reoefrsc el _____      al aftur _____

latelag la _____       zazip al _____

apaps sla traifs _____

Your opinion counts! Use different colors to point out the foods that you like and don't like.

```
L  B  M  A  E  N  H  E  Y  X  Y  X  A  Y
A  B  A  Z  O  L  A  A  R  C  G  E  H  I
G  J  P  Z  W  O  R  G  M  B  R  C  N  C
A  B  N  I  R  P  B  E  J  Z  P  M  Y  X
L  A  S  P  A  P  A  S  F  R  I  T  A  S
L  C  M  A  S  T  R  Q  N  R  Y  C  D  W
E  T  M  L  B  B  U  H  T  Y  E  O  T  K
T  Y  V  V  I  B  G  R  R  R  G  S  S  L
A  U  R  S  N  Q  X  C  F  U  L  R  C  S
O  D  A  L  E  H  L  E  J  A  G  P  S  O
M  O  B  M  W  R  C  L  L  F  L  D  O  Y
K  V  Z  K  V  C  E  R  C  S  X  B  S  P
```

UNIDAD 1 Lección 1 Practice Games

Copyright © by McDougal Littell, a division of Houghton Mifflin Company.

# Palabras escondidas  *Vocabulario en contexto*

You have two tasks in this puzzle. First, use combinations of the scrambled letters
in the following sentence to create as many words from the **Vocabulario** as you can.
Then, unscramble the sentence to solve the riddle.

**Vocabulario:** AL PRAEPRRA MDOCAI

1. _____   4. _____   7. _____

2. _____   5. _____   8. _____

3. _____   6. _____   9. _____

**Riddle:**

Quiero mucho comer.
Pero no sé que hacer.
Tengo queso, vegetales
y salsa.

¿Ahora qué me falta? _____

UNIDAD 1 Lección 1

Practice Games

# Crucigrama *Práctica de gramática 1*

Complete the crossword puzzle with the correct forms of the verb **ser**.

**Verticales** (*down*)

1. tú _____
4. vosotras _____
6. yo _____

**Horizontales** (*across*)

2. él _____
3. nosotros _____
5. ellas _____

# Tic-Tac-Toe *Gramática en contexto*

See who wins at Tic-Tac-Toe by taking turns finding the correct conjugations of **ser** for the subjects listed. Begin by placing an **X** over the appropriate form of **ser** for subject **1**, then continue by marking an **O** over the conjugation for the subject of **2**, and so on.

**X**
1. Él
3. Las niñas
5. Ella
7. Tomás y Miguel

**O**
2. Nosotros
4. doña Carlota
6. Tú
8. Ustedes

| es | es | son |
|---|---|---|
| somos | son | eres |
| es | son | somos |

**Winner: X** *or* **O**?

When you finish, fill in the appropriate sentence with the correct form of **ser**.

If you play by yourself:

**X** _____ el ganador.

OR

**O** _____ el ganador.

If you play with a partner:

Yo _____ el/la ganador(a).

OR

Tú _____ el/la ganador(a).

UNIDAD 1 Lección 1 — Practice Games

Copyright © by McDougal Littell, a division of Houghton Mifflin Company.

# La pirámide de los pronombres *Práctica de gramática 2*

Read the clues. Then, using the letters already provided, complete the pyramid with the correct personal pronouns.

**Clues:**

1. A _____ _____ gusta las botas tejanas.
2. A _____ _____ gusta comer comida china.
3. A _____ _____ gusta ver los videos de terror.
4. A _____ _____ gusta comprar joyas.
5. A _____ _____ gusta estudiar las matemáticas.
6. A _____ _____ gusta correr por las mañanas.

```
              A

          M I __ __

         T __ __ E

       __ L L __ L __

     E __ __ A S L __ __

   V __ S __ __ R __ __ O __

  __ O __ __ T R __ __ N __ __
```

# Rimas *Todo junto*

Read the following poem and circle all of the infinitive verbs you can find.
Then complete the poem by filling in the blanks to describe what you like
and don't like to do.

A Cristina le gusta hablar,
pero no le gusta estudiar.
¿Los libros? ¡Horribles!
¿Los teléfonos? ¡Increíbles!

A Eduardo le gusta correr,
pero no le gusta aprender.
¿El español? ¡Problemático!
¿El fútbol? ¡Fantástico!

A mí me gusta _____ ,
pero no me gusta _____ .
¿_____ ? ¡Malísimo(a)!
¿_____ ? ¡Buenísimo(a)!

**Practice Games**    **UNIDAD 1 Lección 1**

# Actividades favoritas *Lectura cultural*

It's the weekend. Who will be doing what? Cross out the words that don't meet the requirements listed at the beginning of each row. Use the remaining words to write a sentence about what people like to do over the weekend.

| word must have an "n" and an "a" | le gusta | me gusta | les gusta | te gusta | nos gusta |
|---|---|---|---|---|---|
| word must have a "b" and an "l" | estudiar | dibujar | escribir | jugar | hablar |
| word must have an "n" and an "f" | el fútbol | por correo electrónico | por teléfono | en la televisión | un libro |
| word must have a "c" | a | con | para | en | de |
| word must have an "m" and an "o" | las amigas | los amigos | la mamá | el Internet | la escuela |

Secret sentence: _____

# Me gusta... *Repaso*

Follow the clues in each sentence to arrive at the eight letter word that describes what you do in Spanish class. Hint: circle all the letters that the two words from the **Vocabulario** have in common, then eliminate those that are also in the third word.

**Me gusta** ____ ____ ____ ____ ____ ____ ____ ____ .

1. This letter is in **hablar** and **pasear**, but not in **leer**.          ____
2. This letter is in **patineta** and **español**, but not in **tarea**.          ____
3. This letter is in **andar** and **comprar**, but not in **comida**.          ____
4. This letter is in **correos** and **leer**, but not in **dibujar**.          ____
5. This letter is in **televisión** and **andar**, but not in **beber**.          ____
6. This letter is in **comida** and **descansar**, but not in **escuchar**.          ____
7. This letter is in **escribir** and **helado**, but not in **mirar**.          ____
8. This letter is in **tarea** and **fruta**, but not in **patineta**.          ____

UNIDAD 1 Lección 1
Practice Games

Unidad 1, Lección 1
Practice Games

64

¡Avancemos! 1
Unit Resource Book

## ¡Más largo! *Práctica de vocabulario*

Find two words or groups of words from the **Vocabulario** that contain the same letters as the sequence and belong to the category stated.

| | Sequence | Category | Answer |
|---|---|---|---|
| **Modelo:** | ICO | **Adjectives** | *simpático, cómico* |
| 1. | IZA | **Adjectives** | _____ |
| 2. | OSO | **Adjectives** | _____ |
| 3. | AJA | **Adjectives** | _____ |
| 4. | ELO | **Nouns** | _____ |

Now, choose one word from each item. Write a sentence using all these words to describe a person. Then draw the person.

_____

# Adivinanzas *Vocabulario en contexto*

Unscramble the underlined letters in the riddles to find the word that solves each.
Then fill in the blanks to create a poem about yourself.

No me gusta corre<u>r</u>.
<u>Pe</u>ro me gusta <u>c</u>omer,
y mirar la televisión.
No me gus<u>t</u>a ser organi<u>z</u>ado
¡y n<u>o</u> me gusta estudiar!
¿Cómo soy?
Eres _____ .

A <u>e</u>lla le gus<u>t</u>a aprender.
<u>T</u>ambién le gusta escr<u>i</u>bir.
No es <u>n</u>ada perezosa,
más bi<u>en</u> es estud<u>i</u>osa.
<u>E</u>s muy organizada.
¿Cómo es?
Ella es _____ .

A mi me gusta _____ .
También me gusta _____ .
No soy _____ ,
pero yo siempre _____ .
¿Cómo soy?
Soy _____ .

**UNIDAD 1 Lección 2**

**Practice Games**

Unidad 1, Lección 2
Practice Games

**66**

**¡Avancemos! 1**
Unit Resource Book

# Si tienes... *Práctica de gramática 1*

Use the indefinite articles to identify the things that you have (**tienes**) in the spaces provided. Then use the code numbers under the letters to decode the hidden question.

**Si tienes:**          **tienes...**

1.
___ ___ ___ ___ ___ ___ ___ ___
            3                    1   6

2.
___ ___ ___ ___ ___ ___ ___ ___ ___ ___
                  10      8       11

3.
___ ___ ___ ___ ___ ___ ___
4                                   5

4.
___ ___ ___ ___ ___ ___ ___ ___
    7           2                    9

**HIDDEN MESSAGE:** ¿ ___ ___  ___ ___ ___ ___ ___ ___  ___ ___ ___
                       1   2    3   4   5   1   6   7    8   9   5
___ ___  ___ ___ ___ ___ ___ ___ ?
10   2    8   6   11  9   5

# El, la, los y las *Gramática en contexto*

Use the clues to help you solve the scrambled phrases that contain definite articles.

**1.** Este país está en Norteamérica.          sol dtseaos duinso

_____

**2.** Estas son muchas personas.          al ntege

_____

**3.** Es lo que toca un hombre de un grupo.          al rgitarau

_____

**4.** Los vemos por la noche.          al ulan y sal lletreass

_____

**5.** Esta persona es el líder de este país.          le ipsrneedte

_____

**6.** Esta persona te enseña muchas cosas en la escuela.          al rtaaesm

_____

# ¿Cómo son? *Práctica de gramática 2*

Our families and those around us have common characteristics. See if you can guess who these adjectives describe. Some letters have been provided.

1. viejos, cariñosos (*loving*), canosos (*grey-haired*)

   l ___ s a ___ ___ ___ ___ s

2. leal (*loyal*), simpático, joven

   u ___ b ___ e ___ a ___ ___ g o

3. inteligente, trabajadora, simpática

   l ___ m ___ ___ ___ ___ ___ ___

4. pequeño, cómico, simpático

   u ___ p ___ r r ___

# Letras *Todo junto*

Underline the letters that don't belong in the following adjectives. Then unscramble the underlined letters to answer the secret question.

1. Alberto es muy serioso.

2. El estudiante es muy trátabajadoroso.

3. Es un hommbres.

4. Mi abuela es viejia.

5. Ana tiene pielo rupbio.

6. Usted es muy cómmiccos.

¿Cómo somos nosotros? _____

Copyright © by McDougal Littell, a division of Houghton Mifflin Company.

UNIDAD 1 Lección 2

Practice Games

# Código secreto *Lectura cultural*

Use the key to find out what the people below are like.

| A = 🖐 | B = ❀ | C = ☺ | D = ✧ | E = ✳ | F = ❑ |
|--------|--------|--------|--------|--------|--------|
| G = ✿ | H = ○ | I = 👍 | J = ❁ | L = 💧 | M = ☼ |
| N = ★ | O = ✱ | P = ☆ | Q = ✿ | R = ☎ | Rr = ✌ |
| S = ☺ | T = ✶ | U = ↗ | V = ❄ | W = ☽ | X = ✺ |
| Y = ✳ | Z = ❖ |  |  |  |  |

1. Soy una persona muy _____.

2. Ana es una chica _____.

3. Tú eres muy _____.

4. Nosotros somos _____.

5. David tiene _____.

6. Mi mamá es _____.

7. Pedro es un chico _____.

8. La abuelita es muy _____.

# ¿Cómo son? *Repaso*

Match the descriptions on the left with the descriptions on the right. Then write the letters in parentheses in the numbered blanks to reveal the hidden question.

1. A Cristina le gusta leer y hacer su tarea.

2. Miguel y tú nunca limpian sus cuartos.

3. Su mamá trabaja de lunes a domingo.

4. Al profesor no le gusta ser cómico.

5. Los niños del primer grado no son grandes.

6. La señora García y la señora Espinoza hacen ejercicios todos los días.

Sois niños perezosos. (Ó M)

Es una chica estudiosa. (¿ C)

Son niños pequeños. (T)

Son unas mujeres atléticas. (Ú ?)

Es un hombre serio. (E S)

Es una mujer trabajadora. (O E R)

**Hidden question:** ____ ____ ____ ____ ____ ____ ____
( 1 ) ( 2 ) ( 3 ) ( 4 ) (5) ( 6 )

Now use three of the adjectives from the matching activity to answer the secret question in a complete sentence:

_____

UNIDAD 1 Lección 2

Practice Games

Unidad 1, Lección 2
Practice Games

72

¡Avancemos! 1
Unit Resource Book

# Practice Games Answer Key

## PAGE 57
*Práctica de vocabulario*

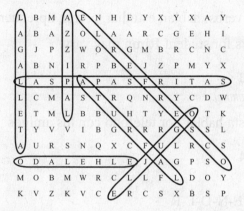

## PAGE 58
*Vocabulario en contexto*

(may be in any order)

1. preparar
2. comer
3. la
4. correr
5. mirar
6. por
7. comprar
8. el
9. comida

Answer to riddle: preparar la comida

## PAGE 59
*Práctica de gramática 1*

### Verticales
1. eres
4. sois
6. soy

### Horizontales
2. es
3. somos
5. son

# Practice Games Answer Key

## PAGE 60
*Gramática en contexto*

|  X  |  O  |
|-----|-----|
| **1.** es | **2.** somos |
| **3.** son | **4.** es |
| **5.** es | **6.** eres |
| **7.** son | **8.** son |

Answers to sentences: es, es, soy, eres

## PAGE 61
*Práctica de gramática 2*

```
              A
          MI M E
          T I T E
        E L L A L E
      E L L A S L E S
    V O S O T R O S O S
  N O S O T R O S N O S
```

## PAGE 62
*Todo junto*

circled verbs: hablar, estudiar, correr, aprender

Answers for student **Rima** may vary.

## PAGE 63
*Lectura cultural*

Nos gusta hablar por teléfono con los amigos.

## PAGE 64
*Repaso*

A-P-R-E-N-D-E-R

UNIDAD 1 Lección 1

Practice Games Answer Key

# Practice Games Answer Key

## PAGE 65
*Práctica de vocabulario*

1. organizado, desorganizado
2. perezoso, estudioso
3. trabajador, baja
4. pelo castaño, pelo rubio

Answers will vary. Possible answer: Mi amigo Cristóbal tiene pelo castaño y es trabajador, estudioso y organizado. Illustration must match sentence. Illustration for this answer might show a boy with brown hair studying with a neat pile of books.

## PAGE 66
*Vocabulario en contexto*

perezoso, inteligente

Poem:

(line 1) infinitive verb

(line 2) infinitive verb

(line 3) adjective that describes a person

(line 4) an action

(line 5) an adjective describing the student, consitant with poem

## PAGE 67
*Práctica de gramática 1*

1. una galleta
2. unos helados
3. unas papas
4. un refresco

Hidden message:
¿TE GUSTAN LOS HELADOS?

## PAGE 68
*Gramática en contexto*

1. Los Estados Unidos
2. la gente
3. la guitarra
4. la luna y las estrellas
5. el presidente
6. la maestra

# Practice Games Answer Key

## PAGE 69

*Práctica de gramática 2*

1. los abuelos
2. un buen amigo
3. la maestra
4. un perro

## PAGE 70

*Todo junto*

1. Alberto es muy serio~~so~~.
2. El estudiante es muy tra~~tá~~bajador~~oso~~.
3. Es un hom~~mbres~~.
4. Mi abuela es viej~~ia~~.
5. Ana tiene ~~pi~~elo ru~~p~~bio.
6. Usted es muy cóm~~miccos~~.

Answer: Somos simpáticos.

## PAGE 71

*Lectura cultural*

1. atlética
2. desorganizada
3. simpático
4. jóvenes
5. pelo rubio
6. pelirroja
7. perezoso
8. baja

## PAGE 72

*Repaso*

¿CÓMO ERES TÚ?

UNIDAD 1 Lección 2

Practice Games Answer Key

HOLT McDOUGAL

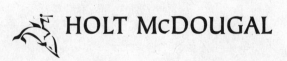

¡Avancemos!

**Video Activities**

# Video Activities *Vocabulario*

## PRE-VIEWING ACTIVITY

Explain what you do on a typical day, starting from when you get home from school. Include snacks, studying and free time activities.

_____

_____

_____

_____

_____

_____

## VIEWING ACTIVITY

Read all the statements below before you watch the video. While you watch, indicate whether each statement is true (T) or false (F) according to the video.

1.  A Miguel le gusta comer.                          T     F
2.  A Alicia no le gusta hablar por teléfono.         T     F
3.  A Alicia no le gusta correr.                      T     F
4.  A Miguel le gusta escuchar música.                T     F
5.  A Alicia no le gusta preparar la comida.          T     F
6.  A Miguel le gusta practicar deportes.             T     F
7.  A Alicia no le gusta mirar la televisión.         T     F
8.  A Alicia le gusta leer libros.                    T     F
9.  A Miguel le gusta beber refrescos.                T     F
10. A Alicia le gusta montar en bicicleta.            T     F
11. A Miguel le gusta descansar.                      T     F
12. A Miguel le gusta comer fruta.                    T     F

# Video Activities *Vocabulario*

## POST-VIEWING ACTIVITY

Use words from the Word Bank to complete the sentences.

| descansar | helado | fruta | preparar | hablar | escuchar | tocar |
|---|---|---|---|---|---|---|

1. A Alicia le gusta _____ por teléfono.

2. A Alicia le gusta _____ la guitarra.

3. A Alicia le gusta _____ la comida.

4. Miguel está en el sofá porque le gusta _____ .

5. A Miguel le gusta comer _____ .

6. A Miguel le gusta _____ música.

7. A Alicia le gusta comer _____ .

# Video Activities *Telehistoria escena 1*

## PRE-VIEWING ACTIVITY

Answer the following questions about what you like to do.

**1** What activities do you like to do outdoors after school?

_____

**2** What activities do you like to do after school when it rains?

_____

**3** What activities do you like to do on the weekend?

_____

**4** What do you like to do with your family?

_____

**5** Based on your answers to the questions above, how would you describe your interests? Are they mostly athletic, intellectual, social, or something else?

_____

## VIEWING ACTIVITY

Read the following list of activities before watching the video. While you watch the video, indicate with a checkmark (🕐) which girl(s) like(s) to do each activity. Hint: there are three activities that neither Sandra nor Alicia like to do. For these activities, write *neither*.

| Sandra | Alicia | |
|---|---|---|
| _____ | _____ | alquilar un DVD |
| _____ | _____ | montar en bicicleta |
| _____ | _____ | andar en patineta |
| _____ | _____ | comer pizza |
| _____ | _____ | pasar un rato con amigos |
| _____ | _____ | trabajar |
| _____ | _____ | dibujar |
| _____ | _____ | hacer la tarea |
| _____ | _____ | jugar al fútbol |
| _____ | _____ | pasear |
| _____ | _____ | hablar por teléfono |
| _____ | _____ | escuchar música |

## Video Activities *Telehistoria escena 1*

### POST-VIEWING ACTIVITY

Match each question with the correct answer based on the video.

1. _____ Alicia, ¿de dónde eres?

   **a.** Sí, pero me gusta más comer pizza.

2. _____ ¿Qué tiempo hace en San Antonio?

   **b.** Sí, no me gusta trabajar los domingos.

3. _____ Sandra, ¿te gusta descansar los domingos?

   **c.** ¡Sí! Me gusta jugar al fútbol.

4. _____ Alicia, ¿te gusta alquilar DVDs y comer papas fritas?

   **d.** Hoy hace sol.

5. _____ ¿Te gusta practicar deportes los domingos?

   **e.** Soy de Miami.

# Video Activities *Telehistoria escena 2*

## PRE-VIEWING ACTIVITY

Answer the following questions.

**1** Where in the United States are you from? For example: the South, the Pacific Northwest, the East Coast.

_____

**2** Have you met anyone from another state who had an accent different from your own? Where had he or she lived?

_____

**3** Can people tell where you are from when you are in a different state? If so, how specifically can they tell? Do they know what city, what state or what region?

_____

_____

**4** Where in the United States do you think people sound the most different from you?

## VIEWING ACTIVITY

Where are Teresa, Miguel, and Mr. Costas from? Before watching the video, read the list of places. Each person is from one of the places on his or her list. Then, while you watch the video, write **es** before the correct country or state from which each person comes, thus creating a complete sentence.

Teresa...

_____ de Panamá.

_____ de Honduras.

_____ de Miami.

Miguel...

_____ de Costa Rica.

_____ de El Salvador.

_____ de Cuba.

Sr. Costas...

_____ de Argentina.

_____ de Florida.

_____ de Colombia.

UNIDAD 1 Lección 1

Video Activities

# Video Activities *Telehistoria escena 2*

## POST-VIEWING ACTIVITY

Indicate if each of the following sentences is (T) for true or (F) for false.

1. Hace sol hoy en Miami.                T     F

2. A Miguel, Teresa y Alicia les gusta pasear.     T     F

3. Teresa y Miguel no son amigos de Alicia.     T     F

4. El señor Costas es la maestra de español.     T     F

5. Teresa no es de Panamá.             T     F

6. Miguel es de El Salvador.            T     F

7. El señor Costas es de los Estados Unidos.     T     F

# Video Activities  *Telehistoria escena 3*

## PRE-VIEWING ACTIVITY

You are a reporter for the school newspaper. It is your job to write a column spotlighting a student in each issue. Write five questions that you might ask the students you interview.

_____

_____

_____

_____

_____

_____

_____

_____

## VIEWING ACTIVITY

Read the following list of activities before watching the video. While you watch the video, indicate with a checkmark (☺) whether Miguel and/or Teresa like to do each activity. Pay attention to what they are *saying* as well as *doing*. Hint: there are two activities that neither Miguel nor Teresa like to do. For these activities, write *neither*.

| Miguel | Teresa | |
|---|---|---|
| _____ | _____ | jugar al fútbol |
| _____ | _____ | correr |
| _____ | _____ | practicar deportes |
| _____ | _____ | comprar libros |
| _____ | _____ | leer libros |
| _____ | _____ | mirar la televisión |
| _____ | _____ | tocar la guitarra |
| _____ | _____ | escuchar música |
| _____ | _____ | comer pizza |
| _____ | _____ | comer helado |
| _____ | _____ | comer fruta |
| _____ | _____ | beber jugos |

# Video Activities *Telehistoria escena 3*

## POST-VIEWING ACTIVITY

Choose the word(s) that best complete(s) each of the following sentences.

**1.** A Miguel le gusta _____ .

   **a.** practicar deportes

   **b.** leer libros

   **c.** comer pizza

**2.** A Miguel no le gusta _____ .

   **a.** tocar la guitarra

   **b.** escuchar música

   **c.** beber jugos

**3.** A Teresa le gusta _____ .

   **a.** mirar la televisión

   **b.** correr

   **c.** tocar la guitarra

**4.** A Teresa no le gusta _____ .

   **a.** leer libros

   **b.** comer fruta

   **c.** escuchar música

**5.** A Teresa y a Miguel les gusta _____ .

   **a.** comer

   **b.** correr

   **c.** viajar

# Video Activities *Vocabulario*

## PRE-VIEWING ACTIVITY

Describe yourself to a new pen pal. Include what you look like, what some of your positive and negative qualities are, and what you like to do in your spare time.

_____
_____
_____
_____
_____
_____
_____
_____

## VIEWING ACTIVITY

Read the phrases below before watching the video. While you watch, indicate with a checkmark (☺) which phrases describe Alberto and which describe Sandra, according to the video. Hint: some of the phrases do not describe either of them. For these phrases, write *neither*.

| Sandra | Alberto | |
|--------|---------|--|
| _____ | _____ | **1.** le gusta dibujar |
| _____ | _____ | **2.** es un(a) estudiante trabajador(a) |
| _____ | _____ | **3.** le gusta correr |
| _____ | _____ | **4.** es simpático(a) |
| _____ | _____ | **5.** le gusta montar en bicicleta |
| _____ | _____ | **6.** es desorganizado(a) |

# Video Activities *Vocabulario*

## POST-VIEWING ACTIVITY

Circle the word(s) that best complete(s) the sentence.

**1.** Sandra no quiere dibujar el hombre alto y un poco _____ .

   **a.** serio

   **b.** chistoso

   **c.** inteligente

**2.** A la chica joven le gusta _____ .

   **a.** jugar al fútbol

   **b.** leer los libros

   **c.** tocar la guitarra

**3.** Alberto piensa que la mujer con pelo _____ es bonita.

   **a.** rojo

   **b.** rubio

   **c.** castaño

**4.** Sandra dibuja un hombre que es _____ .

   **a.** bajo

   **b.** tonto

   **c.** cómico

**5.** A Sandra le gusta dibujar porque es _____ .

   **a.** bonita

   **b.** artística

   **c.** estudiosa

# Video Activities *Telehistoria escena 1*

## PRE-VIEWING ACTIVITY

Imagine that someone you have just met has asked you to tell him about yourself. Write a short paragraph describing yourself to that person. What do you look like? What do you like to do? What type of personality do you have?

_____

_____

_____

_____

_____

## VIEWING ACTIVITY

Read the statements below before watching the video. While you watch the video, write **sí** (*yes*) next to the statements that Alberto or Ricardo *say* about themselves. Write **no** (*no*) next to the statements that they *do not say* about themselves.

### Alberto

_____    No soy alto.

_____    Tengo pelo rubio.

_____    Soy trabajador.

_____    A mí me gusta mirar la televisión.

_____    Soy muy perezoso.

### Ricardo

_____    No soy simpático pero soy estudioso.

_____    Me gusta practicar deportes.

_____    Soy atlético.

_____    Me gusta dibujar y descansar.

_____    Soy un poco artístico.

# Video Activities  *Telehistoria escena 1*

## POST-VIEWING ACTIVITY

Choose the word(s) that best complete(s) each of the following sentences.

**1.** Sandra tiene pelo _____ .

    **a.** rubio

    **b.** castaño

**2.** Ricardo tiene pelo _____ .

    **a.** rubio

    **b.** castaño

**3.** Ricardo y Alberto son _____ de Sandra.

    **a.** hermanos

    **b.** amigos

**4.** A Alberto le gusta _____ .

    **a.** estudiar inglés

    **b.** escuchar música

**5.** Alberto es _____ .

    **a.** trabajador

    **b.** perezoso

**6.** Ricardo es _____ .

    **a.** inteligente y estudioso

    **b.** inteligente y bajo

**7.** A Ricardo le gusta dibujar porque es muy _____ .

    **a.** atlético

    **b.** artístico

**8.** Sandra no es _____ .

    **a.** seria

    **b.** desorganizada

**9.** Sandra es muy _____ .

    **a.** seria

    **b.** cómica

# Video Activities *Telehistoria escena 2*

## PRE-VIEWING ACTIVITY

Answer the following questions about you and a friend.

**1** List five interests that you and your friend have in common.

_____

_____

**2** What are three interests your friend has that are different from your own?

_____

**3** What are three interests you have that your friend does not have?

_____

**4** Do you think having common interests is important when making friends? Why or why not?

_____

_____

## VIEWING ACTIVITY

Read the following statements before watching the video. While you watch, indicate if each of the following sentences is true (T) or false (F).

| | | | |
|---|---|---|---|
| **1.** | A Alberto le gusta beber refrescos. | T | F |
| **2.** | A Sandra le gusta comer helado. | T | F |
| **3.** | Carla y Marta tienen pelo castaño. | T | F |
| **4.** | La amiga de Carla se llama Ana. | T | F |
| **5.** | Ana es una chica muy inteligente. | T | F |
| **6.** | A Ana no le gusta tocar la guitarra. | T | F |

# Video Activities *Telehistoria escena 2*

## POST-VIEWING ACTIVITY

Choose the word(s) that best complete(s) each of the following sentences.

| los libros | escuchar música | estudiantes | helado |
|---|---|---|---|
| jugo | rubio | practicar deportes | |

1. A Ricardo le gusta comer _____ .

2. A Sandra le gusta beber _____ .

3. Marta y Clara son _____ .

4. A Ana le gustan _____ .

5. A Ricardo y a Ana les gusta _____ .

6. A Alberto y a Ana les gusta _____ .

7. Ana tiene pelo _____ .

## Video Activities *Telehistoria escena 3*

### PRE-VIEWING ACTIVITY

Write three sentences comparing the two students below. Then answer the
following questions.

**Fernando**

**Sarah**

_____
_____
_____

**1** Suggest two activities that Fernando might enjoy based on what you know about him.

_____

**2** Which of these two students would most likely be a friend of yours? Why?

_____
_____

### VIEWING ACTIVITY

Read the following adjectives before watching the video. While you watch the video, indicate
with a checkmark (🕐) whether each adjective describes Ana, Alberto, Ricardo, or Trini.
Some adjectives describe more than one person.

| Ana | Alberto | Ricardo | Trini | |
|-----|---------|---------|-------|---|
| ____ | ____ | ____ | ____ | bonito(a) |
| ____ | ____ | ____ | ____ | inteligente |
| ____ | ____ | ____ | ____ | simpático(a) |
| ____ | ____ | ____ | ____ | atlético(a) |
| ____ | ____ | ____ | ____ | cómico(a) |
| ____ | ____ | ____ | ____ | estudioso(a) |
| ____ | ____ | ____ | ____ | diligente |
| ____ | ____ | ____ | ____ | alto(a) |
| ____ | ____ | ____ | ____ | joven |

# Video Activities *Telehistoria escena 3*

## POST-VIEWING ACTIVITY

Complete each sentence with the appropriate word(s).

1. Ana, Alberto y Ricardo son _____ .
2. Alberto y Ricardo son _____ .
3. La mujer es seria, tiene pelo castaño y es _____ .
4. Trini Salgado es _____ .
5. Hoy no es _____ .
6. Un amigo de Alicia es _____ .

a. alta
b. el sábado
c. de México
d. atléticos y cómicos
e. un poco baja
f. inteligentes

# Video Activities Answer Key

## VOCABULARIO

*Page 79*

### PRE-VIEWING ACTIVITY

Answers will vary. Possible answer: When I get home, I eat some crackers and drink a glass of water. Then I do my homework until dinnertime. After dinner, I finish my homework. Then I talk on the phone, send emails and watch television. Before I go to sleep, I read a book for a little while.

### VIEWING ACTIVITY

1. T
2. F
3. F
4. T
5. F
6. T
7. T
8. T
9. T
10. F
11. T
12. F

*Page 80*

### POST-VIEWING ACTIVITY

1. hablar
2. tocar
3. preparar
4. descansar
5. helado
6. escuchar
7. fruta

## TELEHISTORIA ESCENA 1

*Page 81*

### PRE-VIEWING ACTIVITY

1. Answers will vary. Possible answer: I like to play basketball with friends, train with the swim team, and ride my bike in the park.
2. Answers will vary. Possible answer: When it rains I like to play videogames and watch movies on my computer.
3. Answers will vary. Possible answer: I like to go swimming at the neighborhood pool and go to the movies with friends.
4. Answers will vary. Possible answer: I like to watch movies and play board games with my family.
5. Answers will vary. Possible answer: Most of my interests are athletic.

### VIEWING ACTIVITY

alquilar un DVD: Alicia

montar en bicicleta: Sandra

andar en patineta: neither

comer pizza: Sandra / Alicia

pasar un rato con amigos: Alicia

trabajar: neither

dibujar: Sandra / Alicia

hacer la tarea: Sandra

jugar al fútbol: Alicia

pasear: Sandra

hablar por teléfono: Sandra

escuchar música: neither

### POST-VIEWING ACTIVITY

*Page 82*

1. e
2. d
3. b
4. a
5. c

## TELEHISTORIA ESCENA 2

*Page 83*

### PRE-VIEWING ACTIVITY

1. Answers will vary. Possible answer: I am from the South.
2. Answers will vary. Possible answer: A friend who moved from Pennsylvania had a different accent.
3. Answers will vary. Possible answer: People from other states can tell that I am from the South. They cannot tell what state or city.
4. Answers will vary. Possible answer: People in the Northeast sound very different from me.

### VIEWING ACTIVITY

Teresa es de Honduras.

Miguel es de Cuba.

Sr. Costas es de Florida.

### POST-VIEWING ACTIVITY

*Page 84*

1. T
2. T
3. F
4. F
5. T
6. F
7. T

## TELEHISTORIA ESCENA 3

*Page 85*

### PRE-VIEWING ACTIVITY

Answers will vary. Possible answers: Where are you from? What types of sports do you play? What are your favorite school subjects? What are your hobbies? What is your favorite food?

### VIEWING ACTIVITY

jugar al fútbol: Miguel

correr: Miguel

practicar deportes: Miguel

comprar libros: Teresa

leer libros: Teresa

mirar la televisión: Miguel

tocar la guitarra: Teresa

escuchar música: Miguel / Teresa

comer pizza: Teresa

comer helado: Miguel

comer fruta: neither

beber jugos: neither

### POST-VIEWING ACTIVITY

*Page 86*

1. a
2. c
3. c
4. b
5. a

# Video Activities Answer Key

## VOCABULARIO
*Page 87*

### PRE-VIEWING ACTIVITY

Answers will vary. Possible answer: I am tall, with short, curly red hair. I think I am kind and artistic, but I am also a little disorganized, and I can be lazy sometimes. In my spare time, I like to draw, read and go running.

### VIEWING ACTIVITY

1. Sandra
2. Alberto
3. Neither
4. Alberto
5. Neither
6. Alberto

*Page 88*

### POST-VIEWING ACTIVITY

1. a          2. a
3. c          4. c
5. b

## TELEHISTORIA ESCENA 1
*Page 89*

### PRE-VIEWING ACTIVITY

Answers will vary. Possible answer: I am a bit short and very thin. My hair is brown and long and I have green eyes. I am not very athletic. I like to do a lot of things at home. I like to read books, do homework, watch movies and play video games. A lot of people say that I am really intelligent, so I guess you could say that I am. I am a little shy and only have a few good friends. I am introverted.

### VIEWING ACTIVITY

**Alberto**

No soy alto: **si**

Tengo pelo rubio: **no**

Soy trabajador: **si**

A mí me gusta mirar la televisión: **si**

Soy muy perezoso: **no**

**Ricardo**

No soy simpático pero soy estudioso: **no**

Me gusta practicar deportes: **si**

Soy atlético: **si**

Me gusta dibujar y descansar: **no**

Soy un poco artístico: **no**

---

*Page 90*

### POST-VIEWING ACTIVITY

1. a
2. b
3. b
4. b
5. a
6. a
7. b
8. a
9. b

## TELEHISTORIA ESCENA 2
*Page 91*

### PRE-VIEWING ACTIVITY

1. Answers will vary. Possible answer: We both like to play video games, play tennis and basketball together, burn music CDs and ride skateboards.
2. Answers will vary. Possible answer: She likes to read, go skydiving with her parents and play the violin.
3. I like to act, draw and babysit.
4. Answers will vary. Possible answer: Yes, I think it is important to have interests in common with friends so you have things to talk about and do together.

### VIEWING ACTIVITY

1. T
2. F
3. T
4. T
5. T
6. F

*Page 92*

### POST-VIEWING ACTIVITY

1. helado
2. jugo
3. estudiantes
4. los libros
5. practicar deportes
6. escuchar música
7. rubio

---

## TELEHISTORIA ESCENA 3
*Page 93*

### PRE-VIEWING ACTIVITY

Answers will vary. Possible answer: Fernando is taller and older than Sarah. Sarah looks more studious and introverted than Fernando. He is from Chile and she is from the United States.

1. Answers will vary. Possible answer: He might like to play soccer and run marathons.
2. Answers will vary. Possible answer: I would most likely be friends with Fernando because he enjoys sports, like me.

### VIEWING ACTIVITY

bonito(a): Ana

inteligente: Ana, Alberto, Ricardo

simpático(a): Ana, Alberto, Ricardo

atlético(a): Alberto, Ricardo

cómico(a): Alberto, Ricardo

estudioso(a): Ricardo

diligente: Alberto

alto(a): Trini

joven: Trini

*Page 94*

### POST-VIEWING ACTIVITY

1. f
2. d
3. e
4. a
5. b
6. c

# Video Scripts

## VOCABULARIO

**Alicia:** ¡Hola! Buenos días. Me llamo Alicia.

**Miguel:** ¡Hola! ¿Qué tal? Me llamo Miguel. Alicia, ¿qué te gusta hacer?

**Alicia:** Me gusta correr, pero no me gusta montar en bicicleta.

**Miguel:** Me gusta practicar deportes.

**Alicia:** Sí, me gusta jugar al fútbol. Me gusta leer libros, pero no me gusta mirar la televisión.

**Miguel:** Me gusta escuchar música.

**Alicia:** Me gusta preparar la comida.

**Miguel:** Y me gusta comer.

**Alicia:** Me gusta hablar por teléfono y escribir correos electrónicos.

**Miguel:** Y me gusta descansar.

**Alicia:** Pero me gusta tocar la guitarra. Me gusta estudiar y dibujar.

**Miguel:** Alicia, ¿te gusta pasear?

**Alicia:** ¡Sí!

**Miguel:** Alicia, ¿te gusta comer fruta? ¿Beber jugo?

**Alicia:** ¡Sí! Miguel, ¿te gusta comer fruta?

**Miguel:** No, no me gusta comer fruta, y no me gusta beber jugo. Me gusta más comer helado, papas fritas, galletas y me gusta beber refrescos. ¿Y qué? Me gusta comer.

## TELEHISTORIA PROLOGUE

**Paula:** ¡Qué buen gol, Alicia!

**Alicia:** Gracias.

**Sofía:** Nunca te vi jugar así. ¡Jugaste como Trini Salgado!

**Alicia:** Pues sí. Algo aprendí en el torneo la semana pasada.

**Sofía:** ¿El torneo?... ¡es cierto! ¡Los Juegos Juveniles Panamericanos! ¿Cómo estuvieron?

**Alicia:** ¡Genial! El equipo de mi escuela ganó el segundo lugar. Y conocí a muchos chicos y chicas de todo el mundo.

**Alicia:** Sandra, de San Antonio, Pablo de México, Jorge de Costa Rica, Florencia de Argentina, Rodrigo de Puerto Rico, Manuel de Ecuador, Maribel de España y Mario de la República Dominicana. Y...¡conocí a Trini Salgado!

**Sofía:** ¿Trini Salgado?¿De verdad?

**Alicia:** Sí...y nos dio unos consejos sobre fútbol.

**Paula:** ¡Guau!...Trini Salgado, ¡la mejor jugadora de fútbol del mundo!

**Alicia:** Y miren: conseguí esto.

**Paula:** ¡Me encanta!

**Sofía:** ¿Dónde está el autógrafo?

**Alicia:** ¿Qué?

**Sofía:** El autógrafo de Trini Salgado... en tu camiseta...¿lo tienes, verdad?

**Alicia:** No.

**Sofía:** ¿Qué dices, Alicia? ¡No puede ser!

**Paula:** Entonces, tienes una camiseta de Trini Salgado...¿sin su autógrafo?

UNIDAD 1 Lección 1    Video Scripts

# Video Scripts

## TELEHISTORIA ESCENA 1

**Alicia:** Sandra, ¿y qué tiempo hace en San Antonio?

**Sandra:** Hoy hace sol. ¿Y en Miami?

**Papá:** ¿Quién es?

**Alicia:** ¡Papá! Es Sandra.

**Alicia:** ¿En Miami? Hace calor. ¿Te gusta andar en patineta? Perdón.

**Sandra:** No, me gusta más pasear o montar en bicicleta. Los sábados me gusta hacer la tarea. No me gusta trabajar los domingos. Me gusta más dibujar.

**Alicia:** ¿Sí? Los sábados me gusta pasar un rato con amigos....y dibujar, y los domingos, ¡jugar al fútbol! Papá....por favor. Los viernes me gusta alquilar un DVD y comer pizza.

**Sandra:** Sí. Sí, mmmm... me gusta comer pizza y hablar por teléfono.

**Alicia:** ¿Hablar por teléfono? No me gusta hablar por teléfono. Hasta luego.

## TELEHISTORIA ESCENA 2

**Alicia:** ¡Hola!

**Sr. Costas:** ¡Hola!

**Alicia:** Sr. Costas, le presento a dos amigos...Teresa y Miguel. Él es el maestro de español.

**Sr. Costas:** Buenos días. Encantado.

**Miguel:** Hola. El gusto es mío.

**Teresa:** Hola. ¿Cómo está usted?

**Alicia:** Ellos son de...

**Sr. Costas:** ¿Tú eres de... Puerto Rico? ¿Panamá? ¿Costa Rica?

**Teresa:** No, Yo soy de...

**Sr. Costas:** ¿Él es de México? ¿El Salvador? ¿Colombia?

**Miguel:** No, nosotros somos de Cuba y de Honduras. Y usted, ¿de dónde es?

**Sr. Costas:** Soy de...

**Miguel:** ¿Argentina? ¿Chile? ¿Cuba?

**Sr. Costas:** Soy de La Florida. Adiós.

**Teresa, Alicia y Miguel:** Adiós. Hasta luego.

## TELEHISTORIA COMPLETA

**Alicia:** ¿Qué les gusta hacer? ¿Les gusta jugar al fútbol?

**Miguel:** Sí. Me gusta jugar al fútbol o correr. Pero a ella no le gusta practicar deportes.

**Alicia:** ¿Te gusta comprar libros?

**Teresa:** Sí, me gusta comprar libros. Pero a él no le gusta leer.

**Miguel:** Me gusta mirar la televisión.

**Teresa:** No me gusta mirar la televisión. Me gusta más tocar la guitarra o escuchar música.

**Miguel:** Me gusta comer.

**Teresa:** Sí, me gusta comer.

**Alicia:** ¡Nos gusta comer! ¿Qué les gusta comer? ¿Pizza? ¿Les gusta comer helado? ¿Fruta? ¿beber jugos? ¿Y Trini Salgado? ¿Les gusta? ¡Trini Salgado! ¡En San Antonio! ¡Sandra!

# Video Scripts

## VOCABULARIO

**Sandra:** ¡Buenos días! Me llamo Sandra. Me gusta dibujar porque soy una chica artística. Y él es Alberto, un amigo. Es una persona muy buena.

**Alberto:** ¡Hola! ¿Qué tal? Yo soy un estudiante trabajador. No soy perezoso. Yo soy un chico simpático, pero un poco desorganizado. Sandra, ¿qué te gusta dibujar?

**Sandra:** Uh...las personas.

**Alberto:** ¿Un hombre alto y un poco serio?

**Sandra:** Hmmm...no...

**Alberto:** ¿Un estudiante organizado?

**Sandra:** ¿Un chico estudioso? No.

**Alberto:** ¿Una chica atlética y joven? ¿Una mujer bonita? Tiene pelo castaño.

**Sandra:** ¡No! ¡Qué malo eres! No.

**Alberto:** Yo no. Soy bueno. ¡Ah, sí! Un hombre grande, muy cómico y pelirrojo.

**Sandra:** ¿Qué? Sí, muy bien.

## TELEHISTORA ESCENA 1

**Sandra:** Hola, Alicia. Es bonita. Pero te gusta más con el autógrafo de Trini Salgado, ¿no?

**Alberto:** Hola, Sandra.

**Ricardo:** ¿Qué tal?

**Sandra:** ¡Hola! Alicia, te presento a mis amigos: Alberto y Ricardo.

**Alberto:** Hola, Alicia. Me llamo Alberto. Soy alto..., no soy muy alto, tengo pelo castaño, y soy muy trabajador. Pero me gusta mirar la televisión y... escuchar música.

**Sandra:** No, él no es perezoso, pero es un poco desorganizado.

**Ricardo:** Hola, Alicia. ¿Qué tal? Me llamo Ricardo. Soy inteligente, simpático y estudioso. Me gusta practicar deportes porque soy atlético. Y me gusta dibujar porque soy muy artístico.

**Sandra:** Sí. Él es muy artístico.

**Ricardo:** Ella es cómica, ¿no?

**Alberto:** Ella no es muy seria.

**Sandra:** O.K., O.K. Adiós, Alicia. Hasta luego.

## TELEHISTORA ESCENA 2

**Ricardo:** Un helado.

**Alberto:** Unas papas fritas y un refresco.

**Sandra:** Un jugo y una pizza.

**Alberto:** ¿Son las chicas de la clase de la Sra. García?

**Ricardo:** Sí, son Marta, Carla y...

**Sandra:** ¡Ana!

**Ricardo y Alberto:** Ana.

**Alberto:** ¿Quién es ella?

**Sandra:** Ella es una amiga de Carla. Es muy inteligente. Le gusta leer y tocar la guitarra.

**Alberto:** Me gusta escuchar música. Ana, ¿no?

**Sandra:** Sí. Y le gusta practicar deportes.

**Ricardo:** Yo soy atlético. Soy muy bueno.

# Video Scripts

**Sandra:** ¡Ay, los chicos!

**Alberto:** Uhhh Hola. Perdón.

## TELEHISTORA COMPLETA

**Alberto:** Ana es bonita, inteligente y simpática. Y, nosotros somos inteligentes y simpáticos, ¿no?

**Sandra:** Sí, Sí, Uds. son inteligentes, atléticos, cómicos. Ricardo, tú eres estudioso y Alberto, tú eres trabajador.

**Ricardo:** ¿Es Trini Salgado?

**Alberto:** ¿Quién?

**Ricardo:** La mujer seria... tiene pelo castaño.

**Sandra:** No es ella. Es un poco baja. Trini es más alta y más joven. Pero... Es el sábado. Hoy es domingo.

**Ricardo:** Sí, el sábado en San Antonio y el lunes en México.

**Sandra:** ¿México? ¿Puebla, México? Pablo, un amigo muy simpático de Alicia, es de México.

## NIVEL 1, UNIDAD 1

## LECTURA CULTURAL

When the school day is over, Spanish-speaking teenagers find something exciting to do. In Miami the weather is just right for outdoor activities; in Argentina, kids get together to hang out around the city; and in the Dominican Republic, sometimes it gets too hot to be outside. Would you like to find out what they do instead?

## Miami

Teens in Miami enjoy the weather playing soccer, riding bikes, or walking around the city. They can walk to Ocean Drive and admire the Art Deco buildings, a very distinctive architectural style from the 1920's.

Or they skateboard through Lincoln Road, a pedestrian shopping mall closed to traffic, with restaurants and shops, and decorated with tropical plants, pink sidewalks, fountains, and sculptures. This area is known as the creative district of Miami, home to several art galleries and theaters.

## Argentina

In Spanish-speaking cities like Buenos Aires, teenagers walk everywhere. They get together to have a snack, or go to the park to read and play sports. They also like to visit art museums or simply hang out with friends in places like Caminito, where they can meet new people or listen to music.

## Dominican Republic

In the Dominican Republic, Plaza de la Cultura and La Salud Park are always full of people relaxing or exercising. But when the weather is too hot, Dominican teens find indoor spaces to hang out. Just like in the United States, bowling is a very popular pastime among teenagers.

We saw boys skateboarding through Miami streets, we hung out with teenagers in Argentina, and we went bowling with kids in the Dominican Republic. After school activities vary from country to country, but one thing is true everywhere: there is nothing like spending time with friends.

# Audio Scripts

## HOLA, ¿QUÉ TAL?

*Level 1 Textbook pp. 2-3*

*Level 1A Textbook pp. 2-3*

*TXT CD 1, Track 1*

**A.** Hola. ¿Cómo estás?
Bien. ¿Y tú?
Mal.

**B.** ¡Hola, Miguel! ¿Qué tal?
Hola, ¿qué pasa?

**C.** ¡Hasta luego, Ana!
Hasta luego.

**D.** Adiós.
Adiós, señorita.

**E.** Buenos días, señora Ramos.
¿Cómo está usted?
Regular. ¿Y usted?
Más o menos.

**F.** Buenas tardes. ¿Cómo estás?
Muy bien.

**G.** Hola, buenas noches.
Buenas noches, señora.

**H.** Buenas noches, Diana.
Hasta mañana, señor García.

## ¡A RESPONDER!

*Level 1 Textbook p. 3*

*Level 1A Textbook p. 3*

*TXT CD 1, Track 2*

Listen to these people greeting and saying goodbye. Wave toward the front of the room if you hear a greeting or toward the back of the room if you hear a good-bye.

**1.** Buenos días.

**2.** Hasta mañana.

**3.** Adiós.

**4.** ¿Qué tal?

**5.** Buenas tardes.

**6.** ¡Hasta luego!

## PRONUNCIACIÓN

*Level 1 Textbook p. 5*

*Level 1A Textbook p. 5*

*TXT CD 1, Track 3*

La letra **h**

In Spanish, the letter **h** is always silent.

Listen and repeat.

ha
hace
he
helado
hi
hispano
ho
hola
hu

humano
¡Hola, Hugo!
Hasta mañana, Héctor.

## ¡MUCHO GUSTO!

*Level 1 Textbook pp. 6-7*

*Level 1A Textbook pp. 6-7*

*TXT CD 1, Track 4*

**A.** Hola. Me llamo Esteban. ¿Y tú?
¿Cómo te llamas?
Me llamo Diana.
Encantado, Diana.
Igualmente.

**B.** Te presento a Esteban.
Encantada.
Igualmente.

**C.** Perdón. ¿Cómo se llama?
Me llamo Raquel Daza.

**D.** Le presento a Ana Vega.
Mucho gusto.
El gusto es mío.

**E.** ¿Quién es? ¿Es Raúl?
No. Es Juan.

**F.** ¿Cómo se llama?
Se llama Diana.

**G.** ¿Se llama Miguel?
Sí. Se llama Miguel Luque.

## ¡A RESPONDER!

*Level 1 Textbook p. 7*

*Level 1A Textbook p. 7*

*TXT CD 1, Track 5*

Listen to four people make introductions. Point to yourself if you hear someone introducing themselves. Point to the person next to you if you hear someone introducing someone else.

**1.** Te presento a Sonia.

**2.** Hola. Me llamo Ricardo.

**3.** Me llamo Carolina. ¿Y tú?

**4.** Le presento a la señora Vargas.

## EL ABECEDARIO

*Level 1 Textbook pp. 10-11*

*Level 1A Textbook pp. 10-11*

*TXT CD 1, Track 6*

| | |
|---|---|
| A | alfombra |
| Be, be grande | bate |
| Ce | cine |
| De | dinero |
| E | entrada |
| Efe | fruta |
| Ge | gato |
| Hache | helado |
| I | iglú |
| Jota | jabón |
| Ka | karate |
| Ele | lápiz |
| Eme | mochila |
| Ene | nariz |
| Eñe | ñu |
| O | oreja |
| Pe | patines |
| Cu | queso |
| Ere | regalo |
| Erre | guitarra |
| Ese | sofá |
| Te | tiza |
| U | uvas |
| Uve, ve chica | ventana |
| Doble uve, doble ve | wafle |
| Equis | xilófono |
| I griega | yogur |
| Zeta | zapato |

## ¡A RESPONDER!

*Level 1 Textbook p. 10*

*Level 1A Textbook p. 10*

*TXT CD 1, Track 7*

Listen to letters of the Spanish alphabet. Write each letter that you hear on a piece of paper and hold it up.

**1.** ele

**2.** e

**3.** jota

**4.** eñe

**5.** pe

**6.** i

**7.** hache

**8.** be grande

## ACTIVIDAD 8 - Lista

*Level 1 Textbook p. 11*

*Level 1A Textbook p. 11*

*TXT CD 1, Track 8*

Listen to someone dictate an invitation list for a party. Write down each name as it is spelled.

**Modelo:** You hear:

de, a, ene, i, e, ele

You write: Daniel.

**1.** equis, i, eme, e, ene, a

**2.** ge, u, i, ele, ele, e, ere, eme, o

**3.** a, ele, e, jota, a, ene, de, ere, o

**4.** i griega, o, ele, a, ene, de, a

**5.** be grande, e, a, te, ere, i, zeta

**6.** jota, o, ese, e, efe, i, ene, a

**7.** hache, u, ge, o

**8.** te, o, eñe, o

# Audio Scripts

## PRONUNCIACIÓN
*Level 1 Textbook p. 11*
*Level 1A Textbook p. 11*
*TXT CD 1, Track 9*

**Las vocales**

In Spanish, the vowels are **a, e, i, o,** and **u.** Each vowel is always pronounced the same way. Spanish vowels are always short and crisp.

Listen to and repeat these words.

**a,** as in *father*
encantada
mal
mañana
**e,** as in *hey*
menos
señor
presento
**i,** sounds like *meet*
igualmente
adiós
bien
**o,** as in *woke*
hola
noches
cómo
**u,** sounds like *boot*
usted
mucho
tú

## ¿DE DÓNDE ERES?
*Level 1 Textbook pp. 12-13*
*Level 1A Textbook pp. 12-13*
*TXT CD 1, Track 10*

**Señor Costas:** Alicia, ¿de dónde eres?
**Alicia:** Soy de Estados Unidos. ¿De dónde es usted?
**Señor Costas:** Soy de Estados Unidos. Soy de la Florida.
**Alicia:** Pablo es de México.
**Señor Costas:** Isabel es de la República Dominicana.
**Alicia:** Susana es de Costa Rica.
**Señor Costas:** Fernando es de Ecuador.
**Alicia:** Marisol es de Puerto Rico.
**Señor Costas:** Mariano es de Argentina.
**Alicia:** Enrique es de España.

## ¡A RESPONDER!
*Level 1 Textbook p. 13*
*Level 1A Textbook p. 13*
*TXT CD 1, Track 11*

For each statement you hear, point to the person in the photo to whom it refers.

1. Es de Costa Rica.
2. Es de Puerto Rico.
3. Es de Argentina.
4. Es de España.
5. Es de Ecuador.
6. Es de la República Dominicana.

## MI NÚMERO DE TELÉFONO
*Level 1 Textbook p. 16*
*Level 1A Textbook p. 16*
*TXT CD 1, Track 12*

A. ¿Cuál es tu número de teléfono? Es 7-6-4-9-0-8-1.
B. Perdón. ¿Cuál es su número de teléfono? Mi número de teléfono es 2-5-3-7-1-0-9.

## ¡A RESPONDER!
*Level 1 Textbook p. 16*
*Level 1A Textbook p. 16*
*TXT CD 1, Track 13*

Listen to these numbers. If you hear an even number, raise your right hand. If you hear an odd number, raise your left hand.

A. ocho
B. cinco
C. nueve
D. seis
E. cuatro
F. uno
G. diez
H. siete

## LOS DÍAS DE LA SEMANA
*Level 1 Textbook p. 18*
*Level 1A Textbook p. 18*
*TXT CD 1, Track 14*

A. ¿Qué día es hoy? Hoy es jueves.
B. ¿Hoy es viernes? No. Mañana es viernes.

## ¡A RESPONDER!
*Level 1 Textbook p. 18*
*Level 1A Textbook p. 18*
*TXT CD 1, Track 15*

Listen to the days of the week. If you hear a day that you have Spanish class, stand up. If you hear a day that you don't have Spanish class, remain seated.

1. martes
2. domingo
3. lunes
4. miércoles
5. sábado
6. jueves

## ACTIVIDAD 18 - ¿Lógico o ilógico?
*Level 1 Textbook p. 19*
*Level 1A Textbook p. 19*
*TXT CD 1, Track 16*

Listen to these statements about the days of the week. Write **L** if the statement you hear is **lógico** *(logical)* or **I** if it is **ilógico** *(not logical)*.

**Modelo:** You hear: Hoy es viernes. Mañana es domingo. You write: I

1. Hoy es martes. Mañana es miércoles.
2. Hoy es jueves. Mañana es sábado.
3. Hoy es lunes. Mañana es viernes.
4. Hoy es sábado. Mañana es domingo.
5. Hoy es miércoles. Mañana es jueves.
6. Hoy es viernes. Mañana es martes.

## ¿QUÉ TIEMPO HACE?
*Level 1 Textbook p. 20*
*Level 1A Textbook p. 20*
*TXT CD 1, Track 17*

A. Hace calor.
B. Hace sol.
C. Llueve.
D. Hace frío.
E. Hace viento.
F. Nieva.

## ¡A RESPONDER!
*Level 1 Textbook p. 20*
*Level 1A Textbook p. 20*
*TXT CD 1, Track 18*

Listen to weather descriptions. Point to the photo of the person that corresponds to the description you hear.

1. Hace viento.
2. Nieva.
3. Hace sol.
4. Llueve.
5. Hace frío.
6. Hace calor.

Copyright © by McDougal Littell, a division of Houghton Mifflin Company.

# Audio Scripts

## ACTIVIDAD 20 - El tiempo

*Level 1 Textbook p. 21*
*Level 1A Textbook p. 21*
*TXT CD 1, Track 19*

Listen to four meteorologists describe the weather in their region. Write the letter of the photo that corresponds to the weather description you hear.

1. Hace sol.
2. Llueve.
3. Hace viento.
4. Nieva.

## PRESENTACIÓN DE VOCABULARIO

**En la clase**

*Level 1 Textbook pp. 22-23*
*Level 1A Textbook pp. 22-23*
*TXT CD 1, Track 20*

En la clase.

A. Maestro, ¿cómo se dice *Wednesday*?
Se dice *miércoles*.
B. Muchas gracias.
De nada.
C. Perdón. ¿Qué quiere decir *número*?
Quiere decir *number*.

## ¡A RESPONDER!

*Level 1 Textbook p. 22*
*Level 1A Textbook p. 22*
*TXT CD 1, Track 21*

Listen to each classroom instruction and respond appropriately.

1. Abran los libros en la página 10.
2. Levanten la mano.
3. Cierren los libros.
4. Repitan: "buenos días".
5. Saquen una hoja de papel.

## REPASO DE LA LECCIÓN
## ACTIVIDAD 1 - LISTEN AND UNDERSTAND

*Level 1 Textbook p. 26*
*Level 1A Textbook p. 26*
*TXT CD 1, Track 22*

You will hear four separate conversations. Put the drawings in order according to what you hear.

A. Te presento a Victoria. Es de España.
B. ¿Cómo se llama usted?
Me llamo Rodrigo León.
¿Cuál es su número de teléfono?
Cinco-dos-tres-siete-uno-nueve-cero.

C. Abran los libros en la página ocho.
D. Buenos días, señor. ¿Cómo está usted?

## ASSESSMENT SCRIPTS
## TEST CD 1

## PRELIMINARY LESSON TEST: ESCUCHAR ACTIVIDAD A

*Modified Assessment Book p. 1*
*On-level Assessment Book p. 1*
*Pre-AP Assessment Book p. 1*
*TEST CD 1, Track 1*

Listen to the following audio. Then complete Activity A.

**Teacher:** ¿Cómo se escribe tu nombre?
**Pablo:** P-A-B-L-O
**Teacher:** ¿Cómo se escribe tu nombre?
**Emilia:** E-M-I-L-I-A
**Teacher:** ¿Cómo se escribe tu nombre?
**Roberto:** R-O-B-E-R-T-O
**Teacher:** ¿Cómo se escribe tu nombre?
**Luisa:** L-U-I-S-A
**Teacher:** ¿Cómo se escribe tu nombre?
**Miguel:** M-I-G-U-E-L

## ESCUCHAR ACTIVIDAD B

*Modified Assessment Book p. 1*
*On-level Assessment Book p. 1*
*Pre-AP Assessment Book p. 1*
*TEST CD 1, Track 2*

Listen to the following audio. Then complete Activity B.

**Alejandra:** Hola, me llamo Alejandra. Mi número de teléfono es 3-6-2-4-2-9-9.
**Señora Vargas:** Buenos días, me llamo Señora Vargas. Mi número de teléfono es 4-7-3-1-5-1-8.
**Nicolás:** Hola, me llamo Nicolás. Mi número de teléfono es 6-5-7-2-1-3-4.
**Señor López:** Buenas tardes, me llamo Señor López. Mi número de teléfono es 2-7-6-3-0-3-0.
**Diana:** Hola, me llamo Diana. Mi número de teléfono es 4-9-9-2-1-6-1.

## HERITAGE LEARNER SCRIPTS
## HL CD 3

## PRELIMINARY LESSON TEST: ESCUCHAR ACTIVIDAD A

*HL Assessment Book p. 7*
*HL CD 3, Track 1*

Escucha el siguiente audio. Luego, completa Actividad A.

¡Buenos días! Soy Luis Artegui. Artegui se escribe a-ere-te-e-ge-u-i. Soy de España, de Madrid. Y tú eres de México, ¿verdad? Hoy hace frío en Madrid, pero hace sol. ¿Qué tiempo hace en México? ¿Frío o calor? ¿Hace sol o llueve? ¿Cuál es tu número de teléfono? Mi teléfono es 8-7-8-5-3-6-8. ¡Hasta luego!

Buenas tardes. ¿Cómo te llamas? Me llamo Diana Ramírez. Soy hondureña. Soy de Tegucigalpa, Honduras. ¿De dónde eres tú? No eres de Honduras, ¿verdad? Hace calor hoy en Tegucigalpa y también hace mucho viento. Mi teléfono es 2-9-6-6-2-1-4. ¡Hasta mañana!

Hola. ¿Qué pasa? Mucho gusto. Me llamo Roberto Goyoaga. Goyoaga se escribe ge-o-igriega-o-a-ge-a. ¿Cómo te llamas tú? Soy de Santiago. No Santiago, Cuba. Santiago, Chile. ¿Y de dónde eres tú? ¿De Sudamérica? ¿De España? ¿Del Caribe? ¿De México? ¡Contesta mis preguntas, por favor! Hasta mañana.

## ESCUCHAR ACTIVIDAD B

*HL Assessment Book p. 7*
*HL CD 3, Track 2*

Escucha el siguiente audio. Luego, completa Actividad B.

**Sofía:** Buenos días, Sra. Muñoz. ¿Cómo está usted?
**Sra. Muñoz:** Buenos días, Sofía. Estoy muy bien, gracias. ¿Y tú?
**Sofía:** Bien.
**Sra. Muñoz:** Y, ¿quién es?
**Sofía:** ¡Ah! Perdón. Le presento a Ricardo Sánchez.
**Sra. Muñoz:** Mucho gusto, Ricardo.
**Ricardo:** El gusto es mío, señora. ¿Cómo se llama usted?
**Sra. Muñoz:** Soy la Sra. Muñoz. Soy la maestra de español.
**Ricardo:** Muy bien. Y, ¿de dónde es usted?
**Sra. Muñoz:** Soy de México. ¿Y tú?
**Ricardo:** Soy de México también. Soy de la Ciudad de México.
**Sra. Muñoz:** Soy de Guadalajara. Perdón. Tengo clase. Encantada.
**Ricardo:** Encantado. Hasta luego, Sra. Muñoz.
**Sra. Muñoz:** Hasta mañana, Ricardo, Sofía.
**Sofía:** ¡Adiós!

# Audio Scripts

## PRESENTACIÓN DE VOCABULARIO

*Level 1 Textbook pp. 32-33*

*Level 1A Textbook pp. 32-34*

*TXT CD 1, Track 23*

**A:** ¡Hola! Me llamo Teresa. Después de las clases, me gusta pasar un rato con los amigos. Me gusta escuchar música o tocar la guitarra.

**B:** ¡Hola! Me llamo Miguel. A mí me gusta hablar por teléfono, dibujar y estudiar. Me gusta pasear, pero me gusta más correr. A ti, ¿qué te gusta hacer?

**C:** ¡Hola! Me llamo Alicia. A mí me gusta montar en bicicleta y jugar al fútbol. También me gusta andar en patineta.

**D:** Hoy hace calor en Miami. Antes de practicar deportes me gusta comprar agua.

**E:** Me gusta beber agua o jugo pero no me gusta beber refrescos.

**F:** No me gusta trabajar los sábados y domingos. Me gusta escribir correos electrónicos y descansar. También me gusta mirar la televisión. ¿Te gusta pasar un rato con los amigos?

## ¡A RESPONDER!

*Level 1 Textbook p. 33*

*Level 1A Textbook p. 34*

*TXT CD 1, Track 24*

Listen to the list of activities. As you listen, act out the activities.

1. beber
2. descansar
3. hablar por teléfono
4. comer
5. tocar la guitarra
6. leer un libro
7. jugar al fútbol
8. dibujar

## TELEHISTORIA ESCENA 1

*Level 1 Textbook p. 35*

*Level 1A Textbook p. 36*

*TXT CD 1, Track 25*

**Alicia:** En Miami, hace calor. ¿Te gusta andar en patineta?

**Sandra:** No, me gusta más pasear o montar en bicicleta. Los sábados me gusta hacer la tarea.

**Alicia:** ¿Sí? Los sábados me gusta pasar un rato con amigos... ¡y dibujar! Y los domingos, ¡jugar al fútbol! Los viernes me gusta alquilar un DVD y comer pizza.

**Sandra:** Sí, sí. Mmm. Me gusta comer pizza y hablar por teléfono.

**Alicia:** ¿Hablar por teléfono? No me gusta hablar por teléfono.

## TELEHISTORIA ESCENA 2

*Level 1 Textbook p. 40*

*Level 1A Textbook p. 42*

*TXT CD 1, Track 26*

**Alicia:** ¡Hola! Sr. Costas, le presento a dos amigos...Teresa y Miguel. Ellos son de...

**Sr. Costas:** Tú eres de... ¿Puerto Rico? ¿Panamá? ¿Costa Rica?

**Teresa:** No, yo soy de...

**Sr. Costas:** ¿Él es de México? ¿El Salvador? ¿Colombia?

**Miguel:** No, nosotros somos de Cuba y de Honduras. Y usted, ¿de dónde es?

**Sr. Costas:** Soy de...

**Miguel:** ¿Argentina? ¿Chile? ¿Cuba?

**Sr. Costas:** Soy de la Florida.

## PRONUNCIACIÓN

*Level 1 Textbook p. 43*

*Level 1A Textbook p. 47*

*TXT CD 1, Track 27*

Las letras **p** y **t**

When you pronounce the **p** and **t** in English, a puff of air comes out of your mouth. In Spanish, there is no puff of air. Listen and repeat.

pasar

por favor

Puerto Rico

pizza

pero

papas

Pepe prepara las papas fritas.

fruta

televisión

practicar

tocar

estudiar

tarea

¿Te gusta montar en bicicleta?

## ACTIVIDAD 15 (18) – LAS ACTIVIDADES

*Level 1 Textbook p. 44*

*Level 1A Textbook, Act. 18 p. 47*

*TXT CD 1, Track 28*

Copy this chart on a piece of paper. Listen to Mariana's description of what she and her friends like to do on Saturdays, and complete your chart with *sí* or *no*. Then answer the questions.

Hola. Me llamo Mariana. Hoy es sábado. A mis amigos Jorge y Federico y a mí nos gusta descansar. A Federico le gusta pasear pero a Jorge no. Me gusta pasear pero hoy no hace sol. Me gusta más tocar la guitarra. A ellos les gusta escuchar música pero no les gusta tocar la guitarra. A los dos les gusta mirar la televisión. A mí no me gusta mirar la televisión.

## TELEHISTORIA COMPLETA

*Level 1 Textbook p. 45*

*Level 1A Textbook p. 48*

*TXT CD 1, Track 29*

*Escena 1. Resumen.*

A Alicia y a Sandra les gusta hacer muchas actividades. Les gusta dibujar, comer pizza y más.

*Escena 2. Resumen.*

Miguel es de Cuba y Teresa es de Honduras. El señor Costas es de la Florida.

*Escena 3.*

**Alicia:** ¿Qué les gusta hacer?

**Miguel:** Me gusta mirar la televisión.

**Teresa:** No me gusta mirar la televisión. Me gusta más tocar la guitarra o escuchar música.

**Miguel:** Me gusta comer.

**Teresa:** Sí, me gusta comer.

**Alicia:** ¡Nos gusta comer!

**Alicia:** ¿Qué les gusta comer? ¿Pizza? ¿Les gusta comer helado? ¿Fruta? ¿Beber jugos?

**Alicia:** ¿Trini Salgado? ¿En San Antonio? ¡Sandra!

## ACTIVIDAD 20 (23) – INTEGRACIÓN

# Audio Scripts

*Level 1 Textbook p. 47*
*Level 1A Textbook p. 50*
*TXT CD 1, Track 30*

Read the e-mail from Vanessa, then listen to Carmen and take notes. Say what both of them like and don't like.

## FUENTE 2 ESCUCHA A CARMEN

*TXT CD 1, Track 31*

Listen and take notes

- ¿Qué le gusta hacer a Carmen?
- ¿Qué no le gusta hacer?

¡Hola, Vanessa! Me llamo Carmen. Soy de Carolina, Puerto Rico. Después de las clases, me gusta practicar deportes, hacer la tarea o estudiar. No me gusta escuchar música. Y no me gusta mirar la televisión. Los sábados y domingos me gusta pasar un rato con los amigos. Me gusta comer pizza o papas fritas y descansar.

## LECTURA: ¿QUÉ TE GUSTA HACER?

*Level 1 Textbook pp. 48–49*
*Level 1A Textbook pp. 52–53*
*TXT CD 1, Track 32*

This is a survey about what students like to do in their free time. It was conducted among students at a dual-language school in Florida.

¿Qué te gusta hacer?

Me gusta...

mirar la televisión, pasar un rato con los amigos, jugar videojuegos, trabajar, jugar con los amigos, dibujar, practicar deportes, escribir, leer, estudiar, otras actividades.

Resultados de la encuesta. Venticinco estudiantes respondieron a las once categorías o actividades.

Actividades

mirar la tele, pasar un rato, videojuegos, trabajar, jugar, dibujar, deportes, escribir, leer, estudiar, otras.

## REPASO DE LA LECCIÓN: ACTIVIDAD 1 - LISTEN AND UNDERSTAND

*Level 1 Textbook p. 52*
*Level 1A Textbook p. 56*
*TXT CD 1, Track 33*

Listen to Pablo and Sara talk about their activities. Then match the descriptions with the name or names.

**Pablo:** Me llamo Pablo. Soy de Miami. Después de las clases me gusta andar en patineta y escuchar música. Sara es de Puerto Rico. Sara, ¿qué te gusta hacer después de las clases? ¿Te gusta andar en patineta y escuchar música?

**Sara:** ¿Andar en patineta? No, no me gusta andar en patineta. Pero me gusta escuchar música. También me gusta comer frutas.

**Pablo:** ¡Uy! ¡No me gusta comer frutas! Me gusta comer helado.

**Sara:** A mí también. A nosotros nos gusta comer helado. Mmmmmm...

## WORKBOOK SCRIPTS WB CD 1

## INTEGRACIÓN HABLAR

*Level 1 Workbook p. 10*
*Level 1A Workbook p. 10*
*WB CD 1, Track 1*

Listen to what Sofía's mother says about her. Take notes.

## FUENTE 2

*WB CD 1, Track 2*

¡Hola! Me llamo Josefina y soy la mamá de Sofía. A Sofía le gusta hacer muchas cosas los sábados. Pero a ella no le gusta hacer la tarea, no le gusta leer libros y no le gusta estudiar mucho. A ella le gusta comer frutas, helados y beber refrescos, pero no le gusta preparar la comida. A Sofía no le gusta trabajar los sábados y domingos.

## INTEGRACIÓN ESCRIBIR

*Level 1 Workbook p. 11*
*Level 1A Workbook p. 11*
*WB CD 1, Track 3*

Listen to what Lisa says about her weekend activities. Take notes.

## FUENTE 2

*WB CD 1, Track 4*

¡Hola! Soy Lisa. Los sábados, me gusta pasear y pasar un rato con los amigos. También me gusta andar en patineta y jugar al fútbol. Los domingos también me gusta hacer muchas actividades. Pero si llueve, nieva o hace mucho calor,

me gusta más descansar y mirar la televisión.

## ESCUCHAR A, ACTIVIDAD 1

*Level 1 Workbook p. 12*
*Level 1A Workbook p. 12*
*WB CD 1, Track 5*

Listen to the conversation about what these friends like to do. Match each name with the appropriate picture.

**Antonio:** Me llamo Antonio. A mí me gusta jugar al fútbol con mi amigo Raúl. Ángela, ¿qué te gusta a ti hacer los sábados?

**Ángela:** A mí me gusta pasar un rato con los amigos los sábados por la tarde.

**Clara:** Yo me llamo Clara. A mí me gusta más escribir correos electrónicos.

**Roberto:** Me llamo Roberto. A mí los sábados me gusta tocar la guitarra.

## ESCUCHAR A, ACTIVIDAD 2

*Level 1 Workbook p. 12*
*Level 1A Workbook p. 12*
*WB CD 1, Track 6*

Listen to each person say what s/he likes to do. Then read each statement below and say if it is true (cierto) or false (falso).

**Carolina:** Después de las clases, a mí me gusta escuchar música.

**Carlos y Carlota:** A nosotros nos gusta practicar deportes después de la escuela.

**Norberto:** Me llamo Norberto y soy de Argentina. A mí me gusta preparar la comida.

**Gabriel:** Me llamo Gabriel y soy de México. A mí me gusta más correr los sábados y domingos.

## ESCUCHAR B, ACTIVIDAD 1

*Level 1 Workbook p. 13*
*Level 1A Workbook p. 13*
*WB CD 1, Track 7*

Listen to each statement and take notes. Then complete the sentences with the activities they like to do.

**Carolina:** Me llamo Carolina y me gusta escuchar música.

**Carlos:** Yo me llamo Carlos.

# Audio Scripts

**Carlota:** Y yo me llamo Carlota.

**Carlos:** A Carlota y a mí nos gusta practicar deportes.

**Norberto:** Me llamo Norberto. Me gusta preparar la comida con mamá.

**Gabriel:** Me llamo Gabriel. A mí me gusta más correr.

## ESCUCHAR B, ACTIVIDAD 2

*Level 1 Workbook p. 13*

*Level 1A Workbook p. 13*

*WB CD 1, Track 8*

Listen to the conversation and take notes. Then complete the following sentences based on what you heard. Use the words in the box.

**Ricardo:** Me llamo Ricardo. Soy de Honduras. ¿Y tú?

**Laura:** Me llamo Laura. Yo soy de Estados Unidos. Los amigos de la escuela son de Chile.

**Ricardo:** ¡Ah! Felipe y Julia son de México.

## ESCUCHAR C, ACTIVIDAD 1

*Level 1 Workbook p. 14*

*Level 1A Workbook p. 14*

*WB CD 1, Track 9*

¿Qué les gusta hacer? Listen to the conversation between two friends. Take notes and then complete the sentences.

**Ricardo:** Me llamo Ricardo. A mí me gusta pasear y correr después de la escuela. Laura, ¿y a ti?

**Laura:** A mí me gusta más montar en bicicleta. ¿Te gusta más leer un libro o escuchar música?

**Ricardo:** A mí me gusta más escuchar música. ¿Y a ti?

**Laura:** ¡A mí me gusta más dibujar!

## ESCUCHAR C, ACTIVIDAD 2

*Level 1 Workbook p. 14*

*Level 1A Workbook p. 14*

*WB CD 1, Track 10*

Listen to each person's statement. Take notes and then answer the questions in complete sentences.

**Gabriel:** Me llamo Gabriel. Soy de Miami y no me gusta trabajar los sábados. Me gusta más correr.

**Carlota:** Hola, me llamo Carlota. Soy de Bogotá, Colombia y no me gusta

hacer la tarea. ¡Pero sí me gusta la escuela!

## ASSESSMENT SCRIPTS: TEST CD 1

## LESSON 1 TEST: ESCUCHAR ACTIVIDAD A

*Modified Assessment Book p. 11*

*On-level Assessment Book p. 16*

*Pre-AP Assessment Book p. 11*

*TEST CD 1, Track 3*

Listen to the following audio. Then complete Activity A.

**Julio:** Hola, Marta. ¿Qué te gusta hacer después de las clases?

**Marta:** A mí me gusta hablar por teléfono. También me gusta jugar al fútbol. ¿Y a ti, Julio?

**Julio:** A mí no me gusta practicar deportes. A mí me gusta más mirar la televisión y pasar un rato con los amigos.

**Marta:** A mí me gusta comer helado. ¿Y a ti?

**Julio:** ¿Helado? Mmm. ¡Sí!

## LESSON 1 TEST: ESCUCHAR ACTIVIDAD B

*Modified Assessment Book p. 11*

*On-level Assessment Book p. 16*

*Pre-AP Assessment Book p. 11*

*TEST CD 1, Track 4*

Listen to the following audio. Then complete Activity B.

**Juan:** Hola, me llamo Juan. Después de las clases me gusta leer un libro y escribir correos electrónicos. No me gusta mirar la televisión pero me gusta escuchar música. Me gusta tocar la guitarra los sábados. Me gusta beber refrescos y comer papas fritas. ¡También me gusta comer el helado!

## HERITAGE LEARNER SCRIPTS HL CDS 1 & 3

## INTEGRACIÓN HABLAR

*Level 1 HL Workbook p. 12*

*Level 1A HL Workbook p. 12*

*HL CD 1, Track 1*

Escucha el siguiente mensaje. Toma apuntes y responde a las preguntas de manera oral.

## FUENTE 2

*HL CD 1, Track 2*

Te llamo porque necesito urgentemente saber cómo se llama el profesor de música. Necesito llamarlo o escribirle porque en la oficina de matrículas dicen que su clase está llena. Yo necesito esa clase de guitarra flamenca. Llámame pronto, estoy muy preocupada. Chao.

## INTEGRACIÓN ESCRIBIR

*Level 1 HL Workbook p. 13*

*Level 1A HL Workbook p. 13*

*HL CD 1, Track 3*

Escucha con atención el siguiente anuncio. Toma apuntes y luego completa la actividad.

## FUENTE 2

*HL CD 1, Track 4*

¡Educación con emoción! El Club de Veraneo Bahía Kino anuncia su primer concurso de becas. ¿Quieres repasar tus clases mientras montas en motocicleta acuática? ¿Quieres aprender español o inglés mientras descansas en la playa? Educación con emoción. Una alternativa diferente. Escribe una carta y describe tus gustos y preferencias, qué clases te gustaría llevar, por qué eres tú el mejor candidato para recibir la beca. ¡Sólo habrá un ganador y podrías ser tú!

## HERITAGE LEARNER ASSESSMENT

## LESSON 1 TEST: ESCUCHAR, ACTIVIDAD A

*HL Assessment Book p. 17*

*HL CD 3, Track 3*

Escucha el siguiente audio. Luego, completa la Actividad A.

**Juan:** Oye, Isabel. ¿Qué te gusta hacer los fines de semana?

**Isabel:** Bueno, los sábados me gusta pasar un rato con mi amiga Margarita. A nosotras nos gusta pasear y montar en bicicleta. También nos gusta dibujar. Los domingos me gusta hacer la tarea, leer y preparar la comida. Y a ti, ¿qué te gusta hacer los fines de semana?

# Audio Scripts

**Juan:** A mí no me gusta dibujar, pero me gusta montar en bicicleta, escuchar música y tocar la guitarra.

**Isabel:** A Margarita también le gusta tocar la guitarra.

**Juan:** Los sábados y los domingos me gusta jugar al fútbol, mirar el fútbol en la televisión, hablar con los amigos por teléfono y descansar.

**Isabel:** ¿No te gusta estudiar?

**Juan:** No... no me gusta estudiar.

**Isabel:** ¿Y no te gusta leer libros?

**Juan:** Bueno... me gusta leer libros... ¡de fútbol!

**Isabel:** ¡Ay, Juan!

## ESCUCHAR, ACTIVIDAD B

*HL Assessment Book p. 17*

*HL CD 3, Track 4*

Escucha el siguiente audio. Luego, completa la Actividad B.

**Ricardo:** ¡Hola! Soy Ricardo. Antes de ir a la escuela me gusta correr. Después de las clases me gusta descansar, escuchar música y escribir correos electrónicos a los amigos en México. No me gusta hacer la tarea pero me gusta leer. También me gusta hablar por teléfono. Los sábados me gusta pasar un rato con mis amigos. Nos gusta comer pizza, beber refrescos y comprar helados. También nos gusta practicar deportes. Los domingos nos gusta jugar al fútbol y andar en patineta. ¡No nos gusta hacer la tarea! ¿Qué te gusta hacer?

# Audio Scripts

## UNIDAD 1, LECCIÓN 2 TEXTBOOK SCRIPTS TXT CD 1

### PRESENTACIÓN DE VOCABULARIO

*Level 1 Textbook pp. 56-57*
*Level 1A Textbook pp. 60-62*
*TXT CD 1, Track 34*

**A:** ¡Hola! Soy Sandra. Soy artística y tengo pelo castaño. A mi amigo Ricardo le gusta practicar deportes porque es atlético.

**B:** Alberto es trabajador y estudioso. Le gusta estudiar. David es un poco perezoso. No es un estudiante muy bueno. No le gusta trabajar.

**C:** Soy una persona muy organizada. Mi amiga Ana es inteligente pero un poco desorganizada.

**D:** Rafael es muy alto, pero Laura es baja. Manuel es grande, pero Francisco es pequeño. La señora Santa Cruz es un poco vieja, pero Rosita es joven.

**E:** La señora Guardado es pelirroja y el señor Guardado tiene pelo castaño. Marco y Laura son chicos muy buenos. Marco tiene pelo rubio y Laura tiene pelo castaño.

**F:** Yo soy un poco seria, pero mi amigo Alberto es muy cómico. Todos mis amigos son muy simpáticos. ¿Y tú? ¿Cómo eres?

### ¡A RESPONDER!

*Level 1 Textbook p. 57*
*Level 1A Textbook p. 62*
*TXT CD 1, Track 35*

Listen to these descriptions of Sandra and her friends. Point to the person in the photo who matches each description you hear.

1. pelirroja
2. atlético
3. organizada
4. cómico
5. grande
6. perezoso
7. joven
8. trabajador

### TELEHISTORIA ESCENA 1

*Level 1 Textbook p. 59*
*Level 1A Textbook p. 64*
*TXT CD 1, Track 36*

**Sandra:** Es bonita. Pero te gusta más con el autógrafo de Trini Salgado, ¿no?

**Sandra:** Alicia, te presento a mis amigos: Alberto y Ricardo.

**Alberto:** Hola, Alicia. Me llamo Alberto. Soy alto...no soy muy alto. Tengo pelo castaño y soy muy trabajador. Pero me gusta mirar la televisión y escuchar música.

**Sandra:** No, él no es perezoso, pero es un poco desorganizado.

**Ricardo:** Hola, Alicia. ¿Qué tal? Me llamo Ricardo. Soy inteligente, simpático y estudioso. Me gusta practicar deportes porque soy atlético. Y me gusta dibujar porque soy muy artístico.

**Sandra:** Sí. Él es muy artístico.

**Ricardo:** Ella es cómica, ¿no?

**Alberto:** Ella no es muy seria.

**Sandra:** OK, OK. Adiós, Alicia. Hasta luego.

### ACTIVIDAD 6 – LA LISTA DE SANDRA

*Level 1 Textbook p. 62*
*Level 1A Textbook p. 67*
*TXT CD 1, Track 37*

Sandra likes to buy many things. Listen and write a list of what she likes to buy, using *el, la, los, las*.

Me gusta comprar libros, DVDs, frutas, helados, papas fritas, jugo, galletas y pizza.

### TELEHISTORIA, ESCENA 2

*Level 1 Textbook p. 64*
*Level 1A Textbook p. 70*
*TXT CD 1, Track 38*

**Ricardo:** Un helado.

**Alberto:** Unas papas fritas y un refresco.

**Sandra:** Un jugo y una pizza.

**Alberto:** ¿Son las chicas de la clase de la señora García?

**Ricardo:** Sí, son Marta, Carla y...

**Sandra:** Ana.

**Alberto:** ¿Quién es ella?

**Sandra:** Ella es la amiga de Carla. Es muy inteligente. Le gusta leer y tocar la guitarra.

**Alberto:** Me gusta escuchar música. Ana, ¿no?

**Sandra:** Sí. Y le gusta practicar deportes.

**Ricardo:** Yo soy atlético. Soy muy bueno.

**Sandra:** ¡Ay, los chicos!

**Alberto:** Uh... hola. Perdón.

### PRONUNCIACIÓN

*Level 1 Textbook p. 65*
*Level 1A Textbook p. 71*
*TXT CD 1, Track 39*

La letra **ñ**

The **ñ** sounds like the /ny/ in the word *canyon*. The letter **ñ** does not exist in English, but the sound does. Listen and repeat.

señor

España

mañana

pequeño

castaño

La señora es española.

El señor es de España y tiene pelo castaño.

### TELEHISTORIA COMPLETA

*Level 1 Textbook p. 69*
*Level 1A Textbook p. 76*
*TXT CD 1, Track 40*

*Escena 1. Resumen.*

Alberto y Ricardo son amigos de Sandra. Alberto es un poco desorganizado. Ricardo es artístico.

*Escena 2. Resumen.*

Ana es la amiga de Carla. A Ricardo y a Ana les gusta practicar deportes,

Copyright © by McDougal Littell, a division of Houghton Mifflin Company.

# Audio Scripts

y a Alberto y a Ana les gusta escuchar música.

*Escena 3.*

**Alberto:** Ana es bonita, inteligente, simpática... y nosotros somos inteligentes y simpáticos, ¿no?

**Sandra:** Sí, sí, ustedes son inteligentes, atléticos, cómicos. Ricardo, tú eres estudioso y Alberto, tú eres trabajador.

**Ricardo:** ¿Es Trini Salgado?

**Alberto:** ¿Quién?

**Ricardo:** La mujer seria. Tiene pelo castaño.

**Sandra:** No es ella. Es un poco baja. Trini es alta y más joven.

**Sandra:** Pero... es el sábado. Hoy es domingo.

**Ricardo:** Sí, el sábado en San Antonio y el lunes en México.

**Sandra:** ¿México? ¿Puebla, México? Pablo, un amigo muy simpático de Alicia, es de México.

## ACTIVIDAD 19 (23) – INTEGRACIÓN

*Level 1 Textbook p. 71*

*Level 1A Textbook, Act. 23 p. 78*

*TXT CD 1, Track 41*

Read the Web page and listen to the boys' messages. Describe the two boys.

## FUENTE 2

*TXT CD 1, Track 42*

Listen and take notes
- ¿Cómo es Alejandro?
- ¿Qué le gusta hacer?
- ¿Cómo es Édgar? ¿Qué le gusta hacer?

¡Hola! Soy Alejandro. Tengo pelo rubio. No soy muy alto pero no soy bajo. Soy simpático y tengo muchos amigos. Me gusta escribir correos electrónicos. ¿Y tú? ¿Cómo eres? ¿Qué te gusta hacer?

¡Hola! Me llamo Édgar. ¿Y tú? ¿Cómo te llamas? ¿De dónde eres? A mí me gusta escuchar música.

También me gusta escribir correos electrónicos y hablar por teléfono. ¡Hasta luego!

## LECTURA CULTURAL: SALUDOS DESDE SAN ANTONIO Y MIAMI

*Level 1 Textbook pp. 72-73*

*Level 1A Textbook pp. 80-81*

*TXT CD 1, Track 43*

En San Antonio, Texas, hay parques de diversiones, museos, el Paseo del Río y el Álamo. Después de las clases, a los chicos y a las chicas les gusta pasar un rato con los amigos en El Mercado, donde es posible escuchar música de los mariachis y comer comida típica mexicana.

En Miami, Florida, si hace buen tiempo, a los chicos y a las chicas les gusta andar en patineta o montar en bicicleta. Después de las clases, a muchos chicos les gusta pasear con los amigos por la Calle Ocho, en la Pequeña Habana de Miami. ¡Es una pequeña Cuba en la Florida! Allí es posible comer sándwiches cubanos y beber jugo de mango.

## REPASO: ACTIVIDAD 1 – LISTEN AND UNDERSTAND

*Level 1 Textbook p. 76*

*Level 1A Textbook p. 84*

*TXT CD 1, Track 44*

Listen to Carlos talk about himself and his teacher. Then write a description of Carlos and Mrs. Pérez, according to what Carlos says.

Hola. Me llamo Carlos. Soy estudiante de español. Soy alto, pero no soy muy grande. Tengo pelo rubio. Soy un chico cómico, pero soy estudioso. Me gusta aprender el español. La maestra de español es la señora Pérez. Ella es muy buena. También es organizada y trabajadora. Es una mujer pequeña. Es baja y tiene pelo castaño. Le gusta dibujar porque es muy artística.

## COMPARACIÓN CULTURAL: ME GUSTA...

*Level 1 Textbook pp. 78-79*

*Level 1A Textbook pp. 86-87*

*TXT CD 1, Track 45*

**Narrador:** Colombia. José Manuel.

**José Manuel:** Me llamo José Manuel. Soy de Bogotá. Soy cómico y un poco desorganizado pero también soy estudioso. Después de hacer la tarea me gusta jugar al fútbol con mis amigos en el parque El Tunal. También me gusta mirar el fútbol en la televisión.

**Narrador:** Estados Unidos. Martina.

**Martina:** ¡Hola! Me llamo Martina y soy de Miami. Soy inteligente, alta y atlética. Los domingos, me gusta montar en bicicleta. También me gusta preparar jugo de mango o de melón con mi amiga, María. Nos gusta beber mucho jugo porque en Miami hace calor.

**Narrador:** México. Mónica.

**Mónica:** ¿Qué tal? Me llamo Mónica y soy de México, D.F. Tengo pelo castaño y soy seria. Mis amigas Maite y Alejandra también tienen pelo castaño y son muy simpáticas. Maite y yo somos artísticas. Nos gusta tocar la guitarra. También nos gusta dibujar.

## REPASO INCLUSIVO: ACTIVIDAD 1 – LISTEN, UNDERSTAND AND COMPARE

*Level 1 Textbook pp. 80–81*

*Level 1A Textbook pp. 88–89*

*TXT CD 1, Track 46*

Listen to two teen radio reporters talk about typical after-school activities in Miami and San Antonio. Then answer the questions.

**Magdalena:** Buenos días. Yo soy Magdalena Canseco. Después de las clases, a los estudiantes de Miami les gusta pasar un rato con los amigos. Son muy estudiosos pero les gusta más practicar deportes. Les gusta montar en bicicleta y jugar al fútbol. Los estudiantes de Miami son muy atléticos.

# Audio Scripts

Magdalena Canseco, Radio Sol, Miami. David . . .

**David:** Gracias, Magdalena. Soy David Guzmán. En San Antonio, los estudiantes también son atléticos. Les gusta correr y jugar al fútbol. Pero hoy hace calor. Les gusta más leer o descansar. Pero no son perezosos. Los estudiantes de San Antonio son muy trabajadores.

Yo soy David Guzmán, Radio Sol, San Antonio.

## WORKBOOK SCRIPTS WB CD 1

## INTEGRACIÓN HABLAR

*Level 1 Workbook p. 33*

*Level 1A Workbook p. 33*

*WB CD 1, Track 11*

Listen to the principal's description of Arthur over the loudspeaker before his first soccer game. Take notes.

## FUENTE 2

*WB CD 1, Track 12*

¡Buenas tardes a todos los estudiantes!

Les presento a Arthur. ¿Quién es Arthur? Es un estudiante de la escuela. Es un chico trabajador y muy simpático. También es alto y pelirrojo. Sí, y es muy grande, ¿verdad? Es... ¡el número 10!

## INTEGRACIÓN ESCRIBIR

*Level 1 Workbook p. 34*

*Level 1A Workbook p. 34*

*WB CD 1, Track 13*

Listen to the audioclip of a testimonial from Escuela González's Web site. Take notes.

## FUENTE 2

*WB CD 1, Track 14*

**Manuel:** ¡Hola! Yo soy Manuel y me gusta aprender fútbol en la Escuela González, porque es una escuela grande y muy organizada. Los maestros no son perezosos, son muy trabajadores. En la Escuela González, las clases de los hombres y mujeres son serias. Pero las clases de los chicos y chicas son cómicas. Los maestros son simpáticos y también organizados.

## ESCUCHAR A: ACTIVIDAD 1

*Level 1 Workbook p. 35*

*Level 1A Workbook p. 35*

*WB CD 1, Track 15*

Listen to each statement and take notes. Then choose who fits each description below.

**Mario:** ¡Hola! Me llamo Mario y soy de Colorado. Soy alto y tengo el pelo castaño. Me gusta mucho estudiar.

**Claribel:** ¡Buenos días! Soy Claribel de Cancún, México. Soy baja y me gusta trabajar.

**Gustavo:** Soy Gustavo de Puerto Rico. Me gusta dibujar.

## ESCUCHAR A: ACTIVIDAD 2

*Level 1 Workbook p. 35*

*Level 1A Workbook p. 35*

*WB CD 1, Track 16*

Listen to each person describe him/herself. Then read each statement below and say if its true (*cierto*) or false (*falso*).

**Araceli:** ¡Hola! Me llamo Araceli. ¿Cómo te llamas tú?

**Julio:** ¡Hola! Me llamo Julio.

**Araceli:** ¿Qué te gusta hacer, Julio?

**Julio:** Me gusta jugar al fútbol, y las matemáticas. Y, a ti, ¿qué te gusta hacer?

**Araceli:** A mí me gusta dibujar.

**Julio:** ¡Eres artística!

## ESCUCHAR B: ACTIVIDAD 1

*Level 1 Workbook p. 36*

*Level 1A Workbook p. 36*

*WB CD 1, Track 17*

Listen and then draw a line from the people to the adjectives that describe them.

**Enriqueta:** Hola. Me llamo Enriqueta y tengo tres amigos. Ramón es atlético. Le gusta jugar al fútbol. Es alto y pelirrojo. Simón es bajo y muy guapo. Simón es muy desorganizado, porque no le gusta ser organizado. María es muy simpática. También es muy inteligente. Le gusta mucho leer. Ella también es muy estudiosa. Yo soy muy bonita. Tengo el pelo castaño.

## ESCUCHAR B: ACTIVIDAD 2

*Level 1 Workbook p. 36*

*Level 1A Workbook p. 36*

*WB CD 1, Track 18*

Listen to how each person is described. Then complete the following sentences.

**Nancy:** ¡Hola Elena! ¿Quién es ese chico guapo?

**Elena:** ¡Hola Nancy! ¿Quién?

**Nancy:** El chico alto. Tiene pelo castaño.

**Elena:** ¡Ah! Es Melvin. Es un chico muy inteligente, serio y simpático. A él le gusta estudiar. A ti también te gusta, ¿verdad?

**Nancy:** Sí, es verdad, a mí me gusta mucho leer y estudiar. ¿Y quién es el chico bajo?

**Elena:** ¿El pelirrojo?

**Nancy:** Sí, el pelirrojo. Es muy artístico, ¿verdad?

**Elena:** Sí. Se llama Iván. A él le gusta dibujar y tocar la guitarra. Él es muy simpático.

## ESCUCHAR C: ACTIVIDAD 1

*Level 1 Workbook p. 37*

*Level 1A Workbook p. 37*

*WB CD 1, Track 19*

# Audio Scripts

Listen to the dialog and then write three adjectives to describe each of the following people.

**Josué:** ¡Hola Ibelize! ¿Cómo son los estudiantes en la escuela internacional?

**Ibelize:** ¡Hola Josué! Tengo unas amigas nuevas. Son unas chicas muy buenas. Marta y Tania son inteligentes y son muy guapas también. Tienen pelo castaño. Tengo un amigo que se llama Mauricio. Es un poco desorganizado y perezoso, pero es cómico y muy simpático.

**Josué:** ¿Y cómo es la maestra de español?

**Ibelize:** Es la señora Guadalupe y me gusta. Es muy joven y también organizada. Es un poco baja. Es muy guapa y muy inteligente.

## ESCUCHAR C: ACTIVIDAD 2

*Level 1 Workbook p. 37*

*Level 1A Workbook p. 37*

*WB CD 1, Track 20*

Take notes while you listen to the conversation. Then answer the questions in complete sentences.

**Esperanza:** ¡Hola! Me llamo Esperanza. No tengo pelo castaño. Diana tiene pelo rubio. No tengo pelo rubio. Luisa es pelirroja, y yo también. Luisa es baja. Yo soy alta y muy bonita. Diana y Luisa son muy estudiosas. Yo también soy estudiosa. ¿Y tú, cómo eres?

## ASSESSMENT SCRIPTS TEST CD 1

## LESSON 2 TEST: ESCUCHAR ACTIVIDAD A

*Modified Assessment Book p. 23*

*On Level Assessment Book p. 33*

*Pre-AP Assessment Book p. 23*

*TEST CD 1, Track 5*

Listen to the following audio. Then complete Activity A.

**Sra. Estrella:** Hola, soy la señora Estrella. Mis chicas son Ana y Berta. Ellas son jóvenes pero son muy

inteligentes. Son muy trabajadoras y estudiosas. Ana es baja y tiene pelo rubio. Berta es alta y tiene pelo castaño. Ana es muy artística y Berta es muy atlética. Le gusta practicar deportes. También, Ana y Berta son muy bonitas.

## LESSON 2 TEST: ESCUCHAR ACTIVIDAD B

*Modified Assessment Book p. 23*

*On-level Assessment Book p. 33*

*Pre-AP Assessment Book p. 23*

*TEST CD 1, Track 6*

Listen to the following audio. Then complete Activity B.

**Pablo:** Me llamo Pablo. Soy alto, cómico y muy guapo. Tengo pelo castaño. Soy muy inteligente pero no soy estudioso. No me gusta hacer la tarea. Soy artístico. Me gusta dibujar. No soy atlético. No me gusta practicar deportes.

## UNIT 1 TEST: ESCUCHAR ACTIVIDAD A

*Modified Assessment Book p. 35*

*On-level Assessment Book p. 45*

*Pre-AP Assessment Book p. 35*

*TEST CD 1, Track 7*

Listen to the following audio. Then complete Activity A.

¿De dónde eres?

¿Cómo eres?

¿Qué te gusta hacer?

¿Te gusta hablar por teléfono?

¿Qué no te gusta hacer?

## UNIT 1 TEST: ESCUCHAR ACTIVIDAD B

*Modified Assessment Book p. 35*

*On-level Assessment Book p. 45*

*Pre-AP Assessment Book p. 35*

*TEST CD 1, Track 8*

Listen to the following audio. Then complete Activity B.

**Female A:** Hola, ¿cómo estás?

**Female B:** Muy bien, muchas gracias.

**Female A:** ¿Quién es el chico?

**Female B:** Se llama Antonio. Es de México.

**Female A:** Antonio es muy guapo, ¿no?

**Female B:** Sí, es muy guapo. Es alto y tiene pelo castaño.

**Female A:** También es simpático y atlético. Le gusta jugar al fútbol.

## HERITAGE LEARNERS SCRIPTS HL CDS 1 & 3

## INTEGRACIÓN HABLAR

*Level 1 HL Workbook p. 35*

*Level 1A HL Workbook p. 35*

*HL CD 1, Track 5*

Escucha con atención el siguiente audio. Toma notas y prepárate para completar la actividad.

## FUENTE 2

*HL CD 1, Track 6*

Decidí ser candidata este año, porque creo que el puesto de tesorera, el año pasado, me dio la experiencia necesaria para ser presidenta. Aparte, me gusta la actividad política. Me encanta estar ocupada y ayudar. Creo que los estudiantes de la Prepa pueden beneficiarse con mis ideas. La Planilla Verde tiene metas específicas. Creo que lo más importante es la compra de extinguidores de fuego para el laboratorio de química. Ahora sólo tenemos uno y está bueno, pero creo que los estudiantes podemos ayudar con eso.

## INTEGRACIÓN ESCRIBIR

*Level 1 HL Workbook p. 36*

*Level 1A HL Workbook p. 36*

*HL CD 1, Track 7*

Escucha con atención el siguiente audio. Toma notas y prepárate para completar la actividad.

## FUENTE 2

*HL CD 1, Track 8*

Carla: Hola, soy Carla, la hermana de María José. Si escuchas este

# Audio Scripts

mensaje seguramente es porque te interesa contactar a mi hermana. Ella es un poco introvertida y siempre está trabajando, por eso no tiene amigos en Miami. Hace un año que ella vive allá y aquí la echamos mucho de menos. Mi hermana no es muy alta, tiene el pelo rubio y aunque lleva gafas, cuando se las quita se ve bellísima. Si tu eres perezoso o desorganizado, olvídate, no le escribas. Ella es supertrabajadora e inteligente.

## HERITAGE LEARNER ASSESSMENT

## LESSON 2 TEST: ESCUCHAR, ACTIVIDAD A
*HL Assessment Book p. 29*

*HL CD 3, Track 5*

Escucha el siguiente audio. Luego, completa la actividad A.

Enrique es un chico en mi clase de español. Es guapísimo. Tiene pelo rubio muy bonito. No es muy alto, pero es muy atlético. Le gusta mucho jugar al fútbol. Es un estudiante muy bueno porque es inteligente, organizado y trabajador. Es una persona muy estudiosa. ¡No es perezoso! Enrique también es artístico porque le gusta tocar la guitarra. ¡Es el chico más simpático de la clase!

## ESCUCHAR, ACTIVIDAD B
*HL Assessment Book p. 29*

*HL CD 3, Track 6*

Escucha el siguiente audio. Luego, completa la actividad B.

**Mario:** ¡Hola, soy Mario! Lupe y Gloria son dos estudiantes de mi escuela. Las dos son muy simpáticas y muy bonitas. Lupe es bajita y tiene pelo castaño. Gloria es muy alta y tiene pelo rubio. Las dos son inteligentes, pero Lupe es un poco perezosa y no es organizada. No es estudiosa pero es muy atlética porque le gusta practicar todos los deportes. Gloria es más seria y trabajadora. También es muy

organizada y le gusta leer y estudiar. Gloria es artística, pues le gusta dibujar y tocar la guitarra. Las dos son muy buenas amigas.

## UNIT 1 TEST: ESCUCHAR, ACTIVIDAD A
*HL Assessment Book p. 41*

*HL CD 3, Track 7*

Escucha el siguiente audio. Luego, completa la actividad A.

**Ana:** ¿Quién es la maestra de español?

**Miguel:** Es la señora Arias. Doña Antonia Arias.

**Ana:** ¿De dónde es?

**Miguel:** Es de México, de Guadalajara.

**Ana:** ¿Y cómo es ella?

**Miguel:** Es una señora muy organizada y trabajadora.

**Ana:** ¿Es simpática?

**Miguel:** Sí, sí, es muy simpática también.

**Ana:** ¿Qué le gusta hacer?

**Miguel:** Le gusta leer, escribir, tocar la guitarra y dibujar.

**Ana:** Entonces es inteligente y artística. ¿Cómo son sus clases?

**Miguel:** Sus clases son muy buenas. Le gusta preparar sus clases muy bien. Y a los estudiantes les gusta aprender el español con ella. Es una maestra muy buena.

**Ana:** ¡Muy bien!

## ESCUCHAR, ACTIVIDAD B
*HL Assessment Book p. 41*

*HL CD 3, Track 8*

Escucha el siguiente audio. Luego, completa la actividad B.

Roberto es un estudiante de la Escuela Martí en la Florida. Es un chico muy alto y atlético. Le gusta practicar deportes. Los lunes le gusta correr, los martes, montar en bicicleta, los miércoles y los viernes, jugar al fútbol, y los jueves, andar en patineta. Le gusta preparar la comida también. Le gusta comer

pizza, papas fritas y helado y le gusta beber refrescos. No le gusta estudiar porque no es estudioso, pero es muy simpático. Le gusta pasar un rato con los amigos y los sábados les gusta alquilar DVDs, leer libros de fútbol o escuchar música.

Nombre _____ Clase _____ Fecha _____

# Map/Culture Activities *Estados Unidos*

**1** There are many Hispanic communities in the United States. Four are mentioned in the Unit Opener of **Unidad 1**: New York, El Paso, San Antonio, and Miami. Find them on the map. Do you live in one of these cities? Which is closest to where you live?

_____

_____

_____

**2** In the United States there are other cities that also have important Hispanic communities such as Los Angeles, San Diego, Chicago, and Dallas. Find these cities and write their names on the map.

**3** Mexicans form the largest Hispanic group in the United States, in large part due to its proximity. Locate Mexico and label it on the map.

_____

_____

_____

## Map/Culture Activities *Estados Unidos*

Map/Culture Activities

**❶** Are the sentences below true or false? Use the information from the cultural pages in your book to decide. Circle **C** for **cierto** and **F** for **falso**.

   **1.** La ciudad con más latinos en los Estados Unidos es Nueva York.    C    F

   **2.** El Paso, Texas, tiene pocos (*few*) habitantes hispanos.    C    F

   **3.** El mes de la hispanidad empieza (*begins*) el 15 de septiembre.    C    F

   **4.** La pequeña Habana es una comunidad de cubano-americanos.    C    F

**❷** On page 28, your book mentions a few typical Latin American dishes that are eaten in the United States, such as burritos and fajitas. Can you think of any other Latin American dishes that are popular in the United States? Write them below.

_____

_____

_____

_____

_____

_____

**❸** The city of San Antonio holds a ten-day festival to pay tribute to the heros of the Alamo and San Jacinto. Does your town or city have any civic festivals or celebrations? If so, what does it celebrate?

_____

_____

_____

_____

_____

_____

UNIDAD 1

Map/Culture Activities

# Map/Culture Activities Answer Key

## ESTADOS UNIDOS

*Page 113*

**❶** Answers will vary.

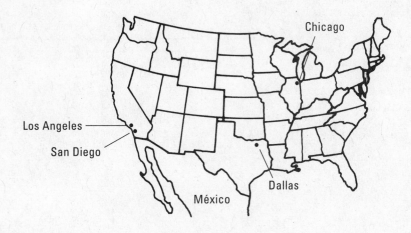

**❷** Students' answers should look like the map above.

**❸** Refer to map above.

*Page 114*

**❶**

| | |
|---|---|
| **1.** C | **2.** F |
| **3.** C | **4.** C |

**❷** Answers will vary, but may include **churros**, **tacos**, **enchiladas**, **quesadillas**, **guacamole**, **salsa**, etc.

**❸** Answers will vary.

# Fine Art Activities

## *Music*, Xavier Cortada

Many artists use colors that are inspired by what they see around them or by what they like most. Observe the painting *Music* by Cuban–American artist Xavier Cortada and answer the following questions.

1. Look at the instruments shown in the painting. Many of these are used in traditional Cuban music. Which instruments are familiar to you? Are there any instruments that you don't recognize? Which instruments do you know how to play? Fill in the following chart with your answers to these questions.

| Instruments I recognize | Unfamiliar instruments | Instruments I play |
|---|---|---|
|  |  |  |

2. Answer the following questions with complete sentences.

a. What did you first think when you looked at *Music*?

_____

b. Do you like the painting? Why or why not?

_____

_____

c. What do you think is the main idea of the painting?

_____

_____

d. How might *Music* relate to Cortada's Cuban-American background?

_____

_____

*Music* (2005), Xavier Cortada. Acrylic on canvas, 60″ x 96″. Courtesy of the artist.

UNIDAD 1 Lección 1   Fine Art Activities

# Fine Art Activities

## *Las hermanas Woloff*, Marta Sánchez

Artists often choose to depict familiar people and places in their paintings. Texas-born Mexican–American Marta Sánchez is a painter especially popular for her close-up depictions of people living in the southwestern United States.

Scan the painting *Las hermanas Woloff* (*The Woloff Sisters*) and answer the following questions with complete sentences.

1. Observe the expressions of the two sisters. What is their mood? What do you think their relationship is like?

_____

_____

_____

_____

2. Imagine that you are going to paint a portrait of a family member. Whose portrait would you choose to paint? What would you call your painting? Describe your portrait in the space provided.

_____

_____

_____

_____

_____

*Las hermanas Woloff* (1996), Marta Sánchez. Courtesy of the artist.

# Fine Art Activities

## Mis hermanos, Jesse Trevino

Mexican-born painter Jesse Trevino is known best for his photorealistic paintings and large murals. Trevino studied briefly in New York before serving in Vietnam, where he lost his right arm. Undeterred by this disability, he went back to school and learned to draw and paint with his left hand. Trevino's paintings appear in the Smithsonian collection of American art, and one of his murals, on the children's museum in San Antonio, Texas, is a city landmark.

Study *Mis hermanos* by Jesse Trevino, and answer the following questions.

**1.** Trevino is noted for his realistic, almost photographic, paintings. Find and list eight details in the painting that make it look life-like.

_____

_____

_____

_____

**2.** What is the story behind this painting? Describe where you think these men are and what you think they are doing. Use details from the painting in your description.

_____

_____

_____

_____

*Mis hermanos* (1976), Jesse Trevino. Acrylic on canvas, 48″ x 70″. Smithsonian American Art Museum, Washington, DC/Art Resource, NY.

# Fine Art Activities

## *Flower Sellers*, Alfredo Ramos Martínez

Alfredo Ramos Martínez led the Mexican mural movement made famous by his colleague, Diego Rivera. Martínez began his career with the help of a wealthy patron who supported him while he studied and painted in Europe. He turned away from European modernism, however, and focused many of his pieces on Mexican culture and traditions. Martínez returned to Mexico and gained fame from his many murals and paintings.

Study *Flower Sellers* by Alfredo Ramos Martínez, and answer the questions below.

1. What is going on in this picture? Describe what you think is the story behind *Flower Sellers*. Use details from the painting in your description.

   _____
   _____
   _____
   _____

2. If you were to paint people hard at work as a representation of the United States, whom would you portray? Why?

   _____
   _____
   _____

*Flower Sellers*, Alfredo Ramos Martínez. Oil on canvas. Image courtesy of Louis Stern Fine Arts, West Hollywood, CA. Christie's Images/SuperStock.

*UNIDAD 1 Lección 2*

*Fine Art Activities*

# Fine Art Activities Answer Key

## MUSIC, XAVIER CORTADA

*Page 117*

1. Answers will vary.
2a. Answers will vary.
  b. Answers will vary.
  c. Answers will vary.
  d. Answers will vary. Students may focus on the Cuban instruments, the importance of music in Cuban culture, etc.

## LAS HERMANAS WOLOFF, MARTA SÁNCHEZ

*Page 118*

1. Answers will vary. The sisters appear content, relaxed, and comfortable with one another.
2. Answers will vary. Students should include title, subject, and a description.

## MIS HERMANOS, JESSE TREVINO

*Page 119*

1. Answers will vary. Possible answers: sunglasses hanging from the shirt; striped and printed shirts; belt buckles; light and shadows across the figures; wristwatch; pleats and creases in pants and jeans; hairstyles; facial expressions.
2. Answers will vary.

## FLOWER SELLERS, ALFREDO RAMOS MARTÍNEZ

*Page 120*

1. Answers will vary. Possible answer: Two women are walking to work where they will sell their flowers. The dark blue sky suggests early morning; their hunched backs and full baskets suggest heavy loads. They are almost trudging under the weight of their burdens. They are not smiling; their faces are serious as they think about the day ahead of them.
2. Answers may vary.

Date: _____.

Dear Family:

We are about to begin *Unidad 1,* of the level 1 *¡Avancemos!* program. It focuses on authentic culture and real-life communication using Spanish in Miami, Florida and San Antonio, Texas. It practices reading, writing, listening, and speaking, and introduces students to culture typical of Miami and San Antonio.

Through completing the activities, students will employ critical thinking skills as they compare the Spanish language and the culture of Miami and San Antonio with their own community. They will also connect to other academic subjects, using their knowledge of Spanish to access new information. In this unit, students are learning to discuss food, art, family traditions, favorite activities, and descriptions. They are also learning about grammar—the verb **ser** (to be), the verb **gustar** (to like), definite and indefinite articles, and noun-adjective agreement.

Please feel free to call me with any questions or concerns you might have as your student practices reading, writing, listening, and speaking in Spanish.

Sincerely,

# Family Involvement Activity

UNIDAD 1

Family Involvement Activity

serio(a)
artístico(a)
estudioso(a)
**grande**

desorganizado(a)
simpático(a)
*inteligente*
bueno(a)

*joven*
**cómico(a)**
viejo(a)
**pequeño(a)**
organizado(a)

**guapo(a)**
perezoso(a)
bajo(a)
**trabajador(a)**

pelirrojo(a)
atlético(a)
bonito(a)
*alto(a)*
**malo(a)**

People have unique traits and personalities that make them individuals. Play this game with your family in order to guess the name of a person by hearing about his or her personal traits.

## STEP 1

Each player must choose three people: one family member, one friend, and one famous person. Write each name on a separate slip of paper and don't tell anyone whom you have selected.

## STEP 2

Write down the participants' names on a piece of paper. Choose a player to begin the first round. Other players must take turns asking yes or no questions about the physical traits, appearance, and personality of the mystery family member. Use the words in Spanish that you have learned from this unit.

## STEP 3

The first player to name the mystery family member correctly wins the round. Continue playing until players have guessed each participant's mystery family member. Then begin a new series of rounds, this time trying to guess the identity of a secret friend. When each player has taken a turn, continue the game by describing and guessing the famous people you have chosen.

Write your scores on the sheet of paper.

# Absent Student Copymasters

## Presentación / Práctica de vocabulario

### Materials Checklist

- [ ] Student text
- [ ] DVD 1
- [ ] Video activities copymasters
- [ ] TXT CD 1 tracks 23–24
- [ ] *Cuaderno* pages 1–3
- [ ] *Cuaderno para hispanohablantes* pages 1–4
- [ ] Did You Get It? Copymasters 29–30

### Steps to Follow

- [ ] Watch the DVD and complete the video activities copymasters.
- [ ] Study the vocabulary by reading the photo captions in **Presentación de vocabulario** (L1 pp. 32–33, L1A pp. 32–34). Listen to TXT CD 1 track 23 to learn about what Miguel and his friends like to do.
- [ ] Practice reading aloud the words in the **Más vocabulario** box (L1 p. 33, L1A p. 34).
- [ ] Complete **Actividades 1** and **2** (L1 p. 34, L1A p. 35).
- [ ] Complete the *Cuaderno* pages 1, 2, and 3.
  OR
  Complete the *Cuaderno para hispanohablantes* pages 1, 2, 3, and 4.
- [ ] Check your comprehension by completing the **Para y piensa** box on page 34 (L1A p. 35).
- [ ] Complete Did You Get It? Copymasters 29 and 30.

### If You Don't Understand . . .

- [ ] Watch the DVD in a quiet place. If you get lost, stop the DVD and replay the section(s) that you didn't understand.
- [ ] Listen to the CD in a quiet place. You may need to listen to the CD several times.
- [ ] Re-read the directions for the activity you find difficult. Rewrite the directions in your own words.
- [ ] Read aloud everything that you write. Be sure that you understand what you are reading.

UNIDAD 1 Lección 1     Absent Student Copymasters

# Absent Student Copymasters

## Vocabulario en contexto

### Materials Checklist

- [ ] Student text
- [ ] DVD 1
- [ ] Video activities copymasters
- [ ] TXT CD 1 track 25
- [ ] Did You Get It? Copymasters 29, 31, and 38

### Steps to Follow

- [ ] Look at the photos on page 35 (L1A p. 36).
- [ ] Read and copy the questions from *Strategies* (L1 p. 35, L1A p. 36).
- [ ] Watch the DVD for **Unidad 1, Telehistoria escena 1** without your book. Then watch the DVD again and complete the video activities copymasters.
- [ ] Follow along with the dialogue in the book as you listen to TXT CD 1 track 25. Try to understand the dialogue using the pictures and the context.
- [ ] Study the words in the **También se dice** box.
- [ ] Complete **Actividades 3**, **4**, and **5** (L1 p. 36, L1A p. 37).
- [ ] Check your comprehension by completing the **Para y piensa** box on page 36 (L1A p. 37).
- [ ] Complete Did You Get It? Copymasters 29, 31, and 38.

### If You Don't Understand . . .

- [ ] Watch the DVD in a quiet place. You may need to watch it several times.
- [ ] Listen to the CD in a quiet place. If you get lost, stop the CD and start it over from the beginning.
- [ ] Write the directions in your own words.
- [ ] Read the model before starting so you know what to do. Imitate the model in your own answers.
- [ ] If an exercise asks you to compare your answer with a partner's, practice both parts.

UNIDAD 1 Lección 1

Absent Student Copymasters

# Absent Student Copymasters

## Presentación / Práctica de gramática

### Materials Checklist

- ☐ Student text
- ☐ *Cuaderno* pages 4–6
- ☐ *Cuaderno para hispanohablantes* pages 5–7
- ☐ Did You Get It? Copymasters 32, 33
- ☐ ClassZone.com

### Steps to Follow

- ☐ Study the subject pronouns and the verb **ser** (L1 p. 37, L1A p. 38).
- ☐ Do **Actividades 6**, **7**, **8**, and **9** (L1 pp. 38–39).
- ☐ Do **Actividades 6**, **7**, **8**, and **9** (L1A pp. 39–40).
- ☐ Complete **Actividades 10** and **11** (L1A p. 41).
- ☐ Complete *Cuaderno* pages 4, 5, and 6.
  OR
  Complete *Cuaderno para hispanohablantes* pages 5, 6, and 7.
- ☐ Check your comprehension by completing the **Para y piensa** box on page 39 (L1A p. 41).
- ☐ Complete Did You Get It? Copymasters 32 and 33.

### If You Don't Understand . . .

- ☐ Re-read the directions for the activity you find difficult.
- ☐ Read the model before starting so you know what to do.
- ☐ In exercises that require a partner, practice both parts.
- ☐ Think about what you are trying to say when you are writing a sentence. Read your sentence aloud to make sure it expresses what you are trying to say.
- ☐ If you have any questions, write them down so you can ask your teacher later.
- ☐ Use the Animated Grammar to help you understand.
- ☐ Use the Leveled Grammar Practice on the @Home Tutor.

# Absent Student Copymasters

## Gramática en contexto

**Materials Checklist**

- [ ] Student text
- [ ] Video activities copymasters
- [ ] DVD 1
- [ ] TXT CD 1 track 26
- [ ] Did You Get It? Copymasters 32, 34

**Steps to Follow**

- [ ] Look at the photo on page 40 (L1A p. 42).

- [ ] Read the *Strategies* (L1 p. 40, L1A p. 42). Try to answer the question in **Cuando lees** before reading the script. Write your answer down.

- [ ] Watch the DVD for **Unidad 1**, **Telehistoria escena 2** without your book. Then watch the DVD again and complete the video activities copymasters.

- [ ] Listen to TXT CD 1 track 26 as you read the text of **Telehistoria escena 2** (L1 p. 40, L1A p. 42).

- [ ] Complete **Actividades 10**, **11**, and **12** (L1 p. 41).

- [ ] Complete **Actividades 12**, **13**, and **14** (L1A p. 43).

- [ ] Check your comprehension by completing the **Para y piensa** box on page 41 (L1A p. 43).

- [ ] Complete Did You Get It? Copymasters 32 and 34.

**If You Don't Understand . . .**

- [ ] Watch the DVD in a quiet place. If you get lost, try reading the dialogue in your textbook as you listen to and watch the DVD.

- [ ] Listen to the CD several times without interruption. If you get lost, try reading along with the CD in the textbook.

- [ ] Re-read the directions for the activity you find difficult and rewrite them in your own words.

- [ ] Study the model at the beginning of the activity. Highlight the different forms of **ser**.

- [ ] If there is an exercise for two partners, practice both parts.

**UNIDAD 1 Lección 1**

**Absent Student Copymasters**

# Absent Student Copymasters

## Presentación / Práctica de gramática

### Materials Checklist

- [ ] Student text
- [ ] *Cuaderno* pages 7–9
- [ ] *Cuaderno para hispanohablantes* pages 8–11
- [ ] TXT CD 1 tracks 27–28
- [ ] Did You Get It? Copymasters 35, 36
- [ ] ClassZone.com

### Steps to Follow

- [ ] Study the uses of the verb **gustar** on page 42 (L1A p. 44).
- [ ] Do **Actividades 13**, **14**, **15**, and **16** (L1 pp. 43–44).
- [ ] Do **Actividades 15**, **16**, **17**, **18**, and **19** (L1A pp. 45–47).
- [ ] Listen to TXT CD 1 track 27 as you follow along in the **Pronunciación** activity on page 43 (L1A p. 47).
- [ ] Complete *Cuaderno* pages 7, 8, and 9.
  OR
  Complete *Cuaderno para hispanohablantes* pages 8, 9, 10, and 11.
- [ ] Check your comprehension by completing the **Para y piensa** box on page 44 (L1A p. 47).
- [ ] Complete Did You Get It? Copymasters 35 and 36.

### If You Don't Understand . . .

- [ ] Listen to the CD in a quiet place. If you get lost, stop the CD and replay it from the beginning.
- [ ] Read the model before starting so you know what to do.
- [ ] In exercises that have parts for two partners, practice both parts.
- [ ] Use the Animated Grammar to help you understand.
- [ ] Use the Leveled Grammar Practice on the @Home Tutor.

UNIDAD 1 Lección 1 Absent Student Copymasters

# Absent Student Copymasters

## Todo junto

### Materials Checklist

- [ ] Student text
- [ ] *Cuaderno* pages 10–11
- [ ] *Cuaderno para hispanohablantes* pages 12–13
- [ ] DVD 1
- [ ] Video activities copymasters
- [ ] TXT CD 1 tracks 29–31
- [ ] WB CD 1 tracks 1–4
- [ ] HL CD 1 tracks 1–4
- [ ] Did You Get It? Copymasters 35, 37

### Steps to Follow

- [ ] Examine the photos and read *Strategies* on page 45 (L1A p. 48).
- [ ] Review the content of **Unidad 1, Telehistoria escena 1** and **escena 2**.
- [ ] Read the script and follow the instructions from the **Cuando escuchas** section. Write down your answer to the question.
- [ ] Watch the DVD for **Unidad 1, Telehistoria escena 3** without your book. Then watch the DVD again and complete the video activities copymasters.
- [ ] Listen to TXT CD 1 track 29 as you read the text of **Telehistoria escena 3** (L1 p. 45, L1A p. 48).
- [ ] Complete **Actividades 17, 18, 19, 20,** and **21** (L1 pp. 46–47).
- [ ] Complete **Actividades 20, 21, 22, 23,** and **24** (L1A pp. 49–50).
- [ ] Complete *Cuaderno* pages 10 and 11.
  OR
  Complete *Cuaderno para hispanohablantes* pages 12 and 13.
- [ ] Check your comprehension by completing the **Para y piensa** box on page 47 (L1A p. 50).
- [ ] Complete Did You Get It? Copymasters 35 and 37.

UNIDAD 1 Lección 1

Absent Student Copymasters

# Absent Student Copymasters

## Lectura y Conexiones

### Materials Checklist

- [ ] Student text
- [ ] TXT CD 1 track 32

### Steps to Follow

- [ ] Read the goal in **¡Avanza!** (L1 p. 48, L1A p. 52).
- [ ] Follow along with the text on TXT CD 1 track 32.
- [ ] Check your comprehension by completing the **¡Interpreta!** and **¿Y tú?** sections of the **Para y piensa** box on page 49 (L1A p. 53).
- [ ] Read **La expedición de Hernando de Soto** on page 50 (L1A p. 54).
- [ ] Calculate the distances in **Proyecto 1**, **Las matemáticas**.
- [ ] Read **El lenguaje** in **Proyecto 2** and try to find three places in the U.S.
- [ ] Read **Proyecto 3**, **La música**. Try to find some Tex-Mex music and describe what you hear.

### If You Don't Understand . . .

- [ ] Listen to the CD in a quiet place. If you get lost, stop the CD and go back.
- [ ] Re-read the directions for the activity you find difficult. Write out the directions in your own words.
- [ ] Read aloud everything that you write. Be sure that you understand what you are reading.
- [ ] If you have any questions, write them down so you can ask your teacher later.
- [ ] If the activity has parts for two people, complete both parts.
- [ ] Think about what you are trying to say when you write a sentence. After you write your sentence, check to make sure that it says what you wanted to say.

UNIDAD 1 Lección 1    Absent Student Copymasters

# Absent Student Copymasters

## Repaso de la lección

### Materials Checklist

☐ Student text

☐ *Cuaderno* pages 12–23

☐ *Cuaderno para hispanohablantes* pages 14–23

☐ TXT CD 1 track 33

☐ WB CD 1 tracks 5–10

### Steps to Follow

☐ Read the bullet points under **¡Llegada!** on page 52 (L1A p. 56).

☐ Complete **Actividades 1**, **2**, **3**, **4**, and **5** (L1 pp. 52–53, L1A pp. 56–57).

☐ Complete *Cuaderno* pages 12, 13, and 14.

☐ Complete *Cuaderno* pages 15, 16, and 17.
OR
Complete *Cuaderno para hispanohablantes* pages 14, 15, 16, and 17.

☐ Complete *Cuaderno* pages 18, 19, and 20.
OR
Complete *Cuaderno para hispanohablantes* pages 18, 19, and 20.

☐ Complete *Cuaderno* pages 21, 22, and 23.
OR
Complete *Cuaderno para hispanohablantes* pages 21, 22, and 23.

### If You Don't Understand . . .

☐ Listen to the CD in a quiet place. If you get lost, stop the CD and go back.

☐ Re-read the directions for the activity you find difficult. Review the hint. Write the directions in your own words.

☐ Read the model before starting so you know what to do. Follow the model. Highlight the verbs in the infinitive.

☐ Read aloud everything that you write. Be sure that you understand what you are reading.

☐ If there is an exercise for two partners, practice both parts.

☐ Think about what you are trying to say when you are writing a sentence. After your sentence is written, check to make sure it says what you wanted it to say.

UNIDAD 1 Lección 1

Absent Student Copymasters

# Absent Student Copymasters

## Presentación / Práctica de vocabulario

**Materials Checklist**

- ☐ Student text
- ☐ DVD 1
- ☐ Video activities copymasters
- ☐ TXT CD 1 tracks 34–35
- ☐ *Cuaderno* pages 24–26
- ☐ *Cuaderno para hispanohablantes* pages 24–27
- ☐ Did You Get It? Copymasters 39, 40

**Steps to Follow**

- ☐ Study the vocabulary from the photo captions in **Presentación de vocabulario** (L1 pp. 56–57, L1A pp. 60–62).

- ☐ Practice the words in the **Más vocabulario** box by reading them aloud. Write the words and their definitions in your notebook.

- ☐ Watch the DVD and complete the video activities copymasters.

- ☐ Listen to TXT CD 1 tracks 34 and 35, and complete the **¡A responder!** activity on page 57 (L1A p. 62).

- ☐ Do **Práctica de vocabulario Actividades 1** and **2** on page 58 (L1A p. 63).

- ☐ Complete *Cuaderno* pages 24, 25, and 26.
  OR
  Complete *Cuaderno para hispanohablantes* pages 24, 25, 26, and 27.

- ☐ Check your comprehension by completing the **Para y piensa** box on page 58 (L1A p. 63).

- ☐ Complete Did You Get It? Copymasters 39 and 40.

**If You Don't Understand . . .**

- ☐ Watch the DVD several times without interruption. It may be helpful to follow along in the text while watching and listening to the DVD.

- ☐ Listen to the CD in a quiet place. Follow along in your text while listening.

- ☐ Reread the activity directions or rewrite them in your own words.

- ☐ Study the model before beginning the activity. Highlight or underline the adjectives.

# Absent Student Copymasters

## Vocabulario en contexto

### Materials Checklist

- [ ] Student text
- [ ] DVD 1
- [ ] Video activities copymasters
- [ ] TXT CD 1 track 36
- [ ] Did You Get It? Copymasters 39, 41.

### Steps to Follow

- [ ] Study the photo on page 59 (L1A p. 64).
- [ ] Read and copy the questions from the **Cuando lees** and **Cuando escuchas** sections of *Strategies* (L1 p. 59, L1A p. 64).
- [ ] Skim the dialogue and review the photo, then write down your answer to the question in **Cuando lees**.
- [ ] Watch the DVD for **Unidad 1**, **Telehistoria escena 1** without your book. Then watch the DVD again and complete the video activities copymasters.
- [ ] Read the text of **Telehistoria escena 2** on page 59 (L1A p. 64) as you listen to TXT CD 1 track 36.
- [ ] Complete **Actividades 3** and **4** (L1 p. 60, L1A p. 65).
- [ ] Check your comprehension by completing the **Para y piensa** box on page 60 (L1A p. 65).
- [ ] Complete Did You Get It? Copymasters 39 and 41.

### If You Don't Understand . . .

- [ ] Watch the DVD in a quiet place. Follow along in the book as you watch and listen to the DVD. Use the pictures and context to help you understand the dialogue.
- [ ] Listen to the CD while reading along in your textbook. Use the picture to help you understand.
- [ ] Review the activity directions. Study the examples given in the text.
- [ ] Underline the adjectives in **Actividad 4**.

UNIDAD 1 Lección 2

Absent Student Copymasters

Unidad 1, Lección 2
Absent Student Copymasters

**134**

**¡Avancemos! 1**
Unit Resource Book

# Absent Student Copymasters

## Presentación / Práctica de gramática

### Materials Checklist

☐ Student text

☐ *Cuaderno* pages 27–29

☐ *Cuaderno para hispanohablantes* pages 28–30

☐ TXT CD 1 track 37

☐ Did You Get It? Copymasters 42–43, 48–49

☐ ClassZone.com

### Steps to Follow

☐ Study the definite and indefinite articles (L1 p. 61, L1A p. 66).

☐ Complete **Actividades 5**, **6**, **7**, **8**, and **9** (L1 pp. 62–63, L1A pp. 67–68).

☐ Complete **Actividades 10** and **11** (L1A p. 69).

☐ Complete *Cuaderno* pages 27, 28, and 29.
OR
Complete *Cuaderno para hispanohablantes* pages 28, 29, and 30.

☐ Check your comprehension by completing the **Para y piensa** box on page 63 (L1A p. 69).

☐ Complete Did You Get It? Copymasters 42, 43, 48, and 49.

### If You Don't Understand . . .

☐ Review the activity directions and study the model. Try to follow the model in your own answers.

☐ Listen to the CD as many times as you need to complete **Actividad 6**.

☐ Make sure that your nouns, verbs, and adjectives agree.

☐ If you have any questions, write them down so you can ask your teacher later.

☐ Use the Animated Grammar to help you understand.

☐ Use the Leveled Grammar Practice on the @Home Tutor.

UNIDAD 1 Lección 2    Absent Student Copymasters

# Absent Student Copymasters

## Gramática en contexto

### Materials Checklist

- [ ] Student text
- [ ] DVD 1
- [ ] Video activities copymasters
- [ ] TXT CD 1 tracks 38–39
- [ ] Did You Get It? Copymasters 42, 44, 50

### Steps to Follow

- [ ] Study the two photos on page 64 (L1A p. 70).
- [ ] Copy the questions from the **Cuando lees** and **Cuando escuchas** sections of *Strategies* (L1 p. 64, L1A p. 70).
- [ ] Read the script and scan the photos for clues about meaning, then try to answer the question from **Cuando lees**.
- [ ] Watch the DVD for **Unidad 1**, **Telehistoria escena 2** without your book. Then watch the DVD again and complete the video activities copymasters.
- [ ] Complete **Actividades 10** and **11** (L1 p. 65).
- [ ] Complete **Actividades 12** and **13** (L1A p. 71).
- [ ] Listen to TXT CD 1 track 39 as you follow along in the **Pronunciación** activity on page 65 (L1A p. 71).
- [ ] Check your comprehension by completing the **Para y piensa** box on page 65 (L1A p. 71).
- [ ] Complete Did You Get It? Copymasters 42, 44, and 50.

### If You Don't Understand . . .

- [ ] Follow along in your book as you watch and listen to the DVD.
- [ ] Listen to the CD in a quiet place. Follow along in your book as you listen to the CD.
- [ ] Listen to the CD and practice speaking until you feel that you are able to pronounce all words from **Pronunciación** correctly. You may need to listen to the CD several times.
- [ ] If you have any questions, write them down so you can ask your teacher later.

UNIDAD 1 Lección 2
Absent Student Copymasters

Unidad 1, Lección 2
Absent Student Copymasters
**136**

¡**Avancemos! 1**
Unit Resource Book

# Absent Student Copymasters

## Presentación / Práctica de gramática

### Materials Checklist

- ☐ Student text
- ☐ *Cuaderno* pages 30–32
- ☐ *Cuaderno para hispanohablantes* pages 31–34
- ☐ Did You Get It? Copymasters 45, 46
- ☐ ClassZone.com

### Steps to Follow

- ☐ Study noun-adjective agreement (L1 p. 66, L1A p. 72).
- ☐ Complete **Actividades 12**, **13,** and **14** (L1 pp. 67–68).
- ☐ Complete **Actividades 14**, **15, 16, 17,** and **18** (L1A pp. 73–75).
- ☐ Complete *Cuaderno* pages 30, 31, and 32.
  OR
  Complete *Cuaderno para hispanohablantes* pages 31, 32, 33, and 34.
- ☐ Check your comprehension by completing the **Para y piensa** box on page 68 (L1A p. 75).
- ☐ Complete Did You Get It? Copymasters 45 and 46.

### If You Don't Understand . . .

- ☐ Review the activity directions and study the model. Try to follow the model in your own answers.
- ☐ Make sure that your nouns, verbs, and adjectives agree.
- ☐ If you have any questions, write them down so you can ask your teacher later.
- ☐ Use the Animated Grammar to help you understand.
- ☐ Use the Leveled Grammar Practice on the @Home Tutor.

UNIDAD 1 Lección 2  Absent Student Copymasters

# Absent Student Copymasters

## Todo junto

### Materials Checklist

- [ ] Student text
- [ ] DVD 1
- [ ] Video activities copymasters
- [ ] TXT CD 1 tracks 40–42
- [ ] WB CD 1 tracks 11–14
- [ ] HL CD 1 tracks 5–8
- [ ] *Cuaderno* pages 33–34
- [ ] *Cuaderno para hispanohablantes* pages 35–36
- [ ] Did You Get It? Copymasters 45, 47

### Steps to Follow

- [ ] Study the large photo on page 69 (L1A p. 76).
- [ ] Copy the questions from the **Cuando lees** and **Cuando escuchas** sections of *Strategies* (L1 p. 69, L1A p. 76).
- [ ] Review the content of **Unidad 1**, **Telehistoria escena 1** and **escena 2**.
- [ ] Read the dialogue and review the photo to help you answer the questions from **Cuando lees**.
- [ ] Watch the DVD for **Unidad 1**, **Telehistoria escena 3** without your book. Then watch the DVD again and complete the DVD activities copymasters.
- [ ] Listen to TXT CD 1 track 40 as you read **Telehistoria escena 3** on page 69 (L1A p. 76).
- [ ] Complete **Actividades 16**, **17**, **18**, **19**, and **20** (L1 pp. 70–71).
- [ ] Complete **Actividades 20**, **21**, **22**, **23**, and **24** (L1A pp. 77–78).
- [ ] Complete *Cuaderno* pages 33 and 34.
  OR
  Complete *Cuaderno para hispanohablantes* pages 35 and 36.
- [ ] Check your comprehension by completing the **Para y piensa** box on page 71 (L1A p. 78).
- [ ] Complete Did You Get It? Copymasters 45 and 47.

# Absent Student Copymasters

## Lectura cultural

### Materials Checklist

- [ ] Student text
- [ ] TXT CD 1 track 43

### Steps to Follow

- [ ] Read and complete **Strategy: Leer** (L1 p. 72, L1A p. 80).
- [ ] Read **Saludos desde San Antonio y Miami** and look at the photos on pages 72 and 73 (L1A pp. 80–81).
- [ ] Follow along with the text as you listen to TXT CD 1 track 43.
- [ ] Check your comprehension by completing the **¿Comprendiste?** and **¿Y tú?** sections of the **Para y piensa** box on page 73 (L1A p. 81).

### If You Don't Understand . . .

- [ ] Listen to the CD as many times as you need to complete the activity.
- [ ] Re-read the directions for the activity you find difficult. Write out the directions in your own words.
- [ ] Say what you want to write before you write it.
- [ ] If you have any questions, write them down so you can ask your teacher later.
- [ ] Read your answers out loud to make sure they say what you wanted to say.

UNIDAD 1 Lección 2     Absent Student Copymasters

# Absent Student Copymasters

## Proyectos culturales

**Materials Checklist**

☐ Student text

☐ Food ingredients from recipe in **Proyecto 1**

**Steps to Follow**

☐ Read **Platos tradicionales de México y Cuba** (L1 p. 74, L1A p. 82).

☐ Look at the photos and read the recipes for **Proyectos 1** and **2**.

☐ Find ingredients for **Salsa fresca** under **Proyecto 1** and combine them according to the recipe.

☐ Complete **En tu comunidad** on page 74 (L1A p. 82).

**If You Don't Understand . . .**

☐ Re-read the directions for the activity you find difficult. Write out the directions in your own words.

☐ If you have any questions, write them down so you can ask your teacher later.

☐ If the activity calls for a partner, complete both parts.

# Absent Student Copymasters

## Repaso de la lección

### Materials Checklist

- [ ] Student text
- [ ] *Cuaderno* pages 35–46
- [ ] *Cuaderno para hispanohablantes* pages 37–46
- [ ] TXT CD 1 track 44
- [ ] WB CD 1 tracks 15–20

### Steps to Follow

- [ ] Read the bullet points under **¡Llegada!** on page 76 (L1A p. 84).
- [ ] Complete **Actividades 1**, **2**, **3**, **4**, and **5** (L1 pp. 76–77, L1A pp. 84–85).
- [ ] Complete **Actividades 1**, **2**, **3**, **4**, and **5** (L1A pp. xx–xx).
- [ ] Complete *Cuaderno* pages 35, 36, and 37.
- [ ] Complete *Cuaderno* pages 38, 39, and 40.
  OR
  Complete *Cuaderno para hispanohablantes* pages 37, 38, 39, and 40.
- [ ] Complete *Cuaderno* pages 41, 42, and 43.
  OR
  Complete *Cuaderno para hispanohablantes* pages 41, 42, and 43.
- [ ] Complete *Cuaderno* pages 44, 45, and 46.
  OR
  Complete *Cuaderno para hispanohablantes* pages 44, 45, and 46.

### If You Don't Understand . . .

- [ ] For activities that require the CD, listen to the CD in a quiet place. If you get lost, stop the CD and go back.
- [ ] Re-read the directions for the activity you find difficult. Write out the directions in your own words.
- [ ] Write the model on your paper. Try to follow the model in your own answers.
- [ ] Read everything aloud. Be sure that you understand what you are reading.
- [ ] If you have any questions, write them down for your teacher to answer later.
- [ ] Read your answers aloud to make sure they say what you wanted to say.

UNIDAD 1 Lección 2    Absent Student Copymasters

# Absent Student Copymasters

## Comparación cultural

### Materials Checklist

☐ Student text

☐ TXT CD 1 track 45

### Steps to Follow

☐ Read the directions in **Lectura y Escritura** for **Actividades 1** and **2** (L1 p. 78, L1A p. 86).

☐ Listen to TXT CD 1 track 45 as you read along in the text **Me gusta…** (L1 p. 78, L1A p. 87).

☐ Read the Strategy for **Escribir**, then begin **Actividad 2**.

☐ Complete the **Compara con tu mundo** section (L1 p. 78, L1A p. 86).

### If You Don't Understand . . .

☐ Read through all of the instructions before you begin reading the feature.

☐ Listen to the CD in a quiet place. Pause and go back as often as necessary.

☐ Look up words you don't know.

☐ Make a list of questions if you are confused or don't know how to say something. Think of what you do know how to say.

☐ Think about what you want to say before you begin writing. Read everything you write to make sure it is clear.

**UNIDAD 1 Lección 2**

**Absent Student Copymasters**

# Absent Student Copymasters

*Level 1* pp. 80–81
*Level 1A* pp. 88–89

## Repaso inclusivo

**Materials Checklist**

- [ ] Student text
- [ ] TXT CD 1 track 46

**Steps to Follow**

- [ ] Go over the Options for Review, **Actividades 1**, **2**, **3**, **4**, **5**, **6**, and **7** (L1 pp. 80–81, L1A pp. 88–89).
- [ ] Listen to TXT CD 1 track 46 for **Actividad 1** on page 80 (L1A p. 88). Answer the questions.
- [ ] Prepare an oral presentation for **Actividad 2** on page 80 (L1A p. 88).
- [ ] Create a yearbook entry for yourself for **Actividad 4** on page 80 (L1A p. 89).
- [ ] Write a personal profile for the student described in **Actividad 7** on page 81 (L1A **Actividad 6**, p. 89).

**If You Don't Understand . . .**

- [ ] Do the activities you understand first.
- [ ] Listen to the CD as many times as you need to complete **Actividad 1**.
- [ ] Re-read the directions for the activity you find difficult. Write out the directions in your own words.
- [ ] Say what you want to write before you write it.
- [ ] If you have any questions, write them down so you can ask your teacher later.
- [ ] Practice both parts of any partner activities.
- [ ] After you write a sentence, check to make sure that it says what you wanted to say.

UNIDAD 1 Lección 2   Absent Student Copymasters

Copyright © by McDougal Littell, a division of Houghton Mifflin Company.